ACKNOWLEDGEMENTS

We wish to thank the following who have contributed
to the success of this year's competition:

THE JUDGES
Joyce Douglas, Sian Harrison, Zindika Macheol,
David Muir, Lascelles Udenzie and Mervyn Weir.

PRIZE CONTRIBUTORS
Caribbean Times
Longman Group UK Limited
New Zealand High Commission
Penguin Books
Sierra Leone High Commission
The Women's Press
Timbuktu Books
Virago Press
Voice Newspapers
Mr. A. Odoom
M. & Mme. P. Salmon
Mr. J. Thomas
Trix Worrell

ADMINISTRATION
Mary Atkins, Eme Bassey, Lottie Betts-Priddy, Linda Jones,
Hyacinth Meerabux, Mia Morris, and Jacqueline Williams.

PRODUCTION
Paulo Araujo, Anthony Betts, Frank Hams, Bernard Osborne,
Karl Russell, Michael Stanbury and Mervyn Weir.

CONTENTS

CREATIVE WRITING • 10-15

CREATIVE WRITING • 16-19

CREATIVE WRITING • 20-30

INTRODUCTION

"I have a dream that one day this nation will rise up and live out the true meaning of its creed: 'We hold these truths to be self evident; that all men are created equal.' ...I have a dream that my four little children will one day live in a nation where they will not be judged by the colour of their skin but by the content of their character..."

These famous words, spoken in the rich and resonant voice of America's greatest Civil Rights leader in 1963, echo down the corridors of time and pierce our consciousness too, on this side of the Atlantic. King's dream did not die with him. His life, courage and example have inspired countless others and still stir us today.

This volume of ACER'S Black Young Writers Winning Essays is dedicated to Martin Luther King for daring to dream when there appeared to be no hope and for fighting so courageously with no weapons except the awesome and powerful arsenal of belief in God, belief in the destiny of his people and belief in himself.

The Afro-Caribbean Education Resource Centre (ACER), like many other community initiatives was founded on the dreams, aspirations and determination of its founders. Twelve years ago, ACER dared to dream of an Education system that would not fail our children; of a society that would value the culture and traditions of Black people and that would give our children equal opportunities to fulfil their considerable potential.

The institutional racism which is endemic in a euro-centric curriculum has created a system that legislates against Black children on many levels. From its inception, ACER'S rationale has been to provide alternative structures, strategies and resources to counter this. One of our earliest initiatives was the establishing of a writing competition that would specifically give Black, young people a forum in which their articulate voices could be heard on a range of issues that was relevant to them.

i

The success of this competition over the years is impossible to quantify. How do you measure the joy of self expression - at last released? How do you measure the pride that exudes from seeing your writing printed and published? How do you measure the confidence that's built and reinforced on having your work validated and celebrated by educationalists and the community at large? We at ACER are happy and proud to have published eleven volumes of essays and to have provided a starting point from which many a successful career has been launched.

However, our dream is in trouble. This may well be the last year of the Writing Awards as we know it. At the time of going to press the future of ACER is uncertain due to the imminent abolition of the Inner London Education Authority. We have published this present volume amid the anxiety and stress that a volatile situation engenders.

We need not worry. Dr. King reminds us that: "Shattered dreams are a hallmark of our mortal life" and reassures us that, "We must accept finite disappointment but we must never lose infinite hope." And why should we lose hope when this volume of essays testify that yet another generation of young Black people have caught Dr. King's vision? In the words of Bernadette Francis: "We're going to have to wait a long time. But we musn't give up, for if we do we shall lose all that the great leader fought for."

The transfer of King's vision is demonstated in the writing of Arthur Hamilton: "I sincerely hope that the Black church will finally manage to combine its spiritual message with a strong, powerful and active social one... If the Black church is indeed following the pattern of Jesus Christ, then it must speak out for the oppressed, the poor the disadvantaged..." Years before, King had told us: "The church cannot be silent while mankind faces the threat of nuclear annihilation..." and "A religion true to its nature must also be concerned about man's social conditions."

Martin Luther King has been an enduring and powerful role model on an international level but Deirdre Woods argues that our most positive, yet underrated role models are the women who in their myriad ways have brought us up. "Instead of 'setting up' our daughters for disillusionment and disappointment by adopting 'stars' as positive role models, let us look to the women who have and will always be the backbone of our race. I am referring to our mothers, grandmothers, sisters, aunts..."

In spite of such positve influences we still hear the poignant plea of Michelle Matty as she asks: "I often wonder where I fit in, where I belong, can you tell me?" Lynette Charles tells us in no uncertain terms that: "I still think that racism is practised daily in Britain. It is to be seen in all areas of life. I believe this makes Black people feel powerless. No one can deny the racist attitude shown by the media where Black people are seen to be the problem or just not visible." Victor Amokeodo in a biting and informative analysis of international aid states: "The poorer countries have been made pawns in the ideological wars of today through foreign aid."

So, whether on a personal, national or international level, these writings provide insight, analysis and hope. Martin Luther King's dream is alive and well though far from being fulfilled. Lynette Charles tells us again: "In Britain Today, Martin's dream has partly been fulfilled because we can now find Black people in important jobs, for example we have four Black Members in Parliament and in many other important roles.

This optimistic note augurs well for the future and we are encouraged with the words of Dr. King: "We are going on...Let us rise up tonight with a greater readiness. Let us stand with a greater determination...I don't know what will happen now. We've got some difficult days ahead. But it doesn't matter with me now, because I've been to the mountain top...I want you to know that we as a people will get to the promised land.."

MERVYN WEIR
January 1990

WINNING ESSAYS
AGE 10-15

LYNETTE CHARLES
1st Place • Essays
Age 14

HAS MARTIN LUTHER KING'S DREAM BEEN FULFILLED?

Martin Luther King Junior was born in Atlanta Georgia in 1929. He first came to prominence during the period when Black people boycotted the buses in Montgomery, Alabama, where he was serving as a minister. The boycott started when a 43 year old negro seamstress, Rosa Parks, feeling too tired to stand in the negro section at the rear of the bus, sat in the front seat (where she was not supposed to) and refused to give up her seat when asked to do so by a white man. She was arrested and jailed.

At once several Black leaders in Montgomery began preparing to have Rosa Parks defended in court and as a protest, a boycott of all the buses in the city was organised. Martin Luther King was asked to head the movement, which led to similar boycotts and freedom riots all over the South. As a result, Martin Luther King became a national figure.

Martin Luther King perhaps gained his inspiration from this incident and went on to voice feelings which were not only his own but became the voice of all Black Americans. The negro boycott of the bus company which later led to the abolition of racial segregation on the buses.

In his speeches Martin aroused the gathering and transported the crowd to a very high pitch. The dream which he portrayed to his people went like this. "I have a dream that one day even the state of Mississippi, a desert sweltering with heat of injustice and oppression will be

1

transformed into an oasis of freedom and justice. I have a dream that my little children will one day live in a nation where they will not be judged by the colour of their skin, but by the content of their character. I have a dream today.

"I have a dream today that one day the state of Alabama, whose governor's lips are presently dripping with the words of interposition and nullification, will be transformed into a situation where little Black boys and little white girls can walk together as sisters and brothers. I have a dream that one day every valley shall be exalted, every hill and mountain will be made low, the rough places will be made straight and the glory of God shall be revealed, and all flesh shall see it together."

If one were to examine King's speech one would be justified to say that significant changes and improvements have been made in the lives and status of Black people in America. Black people are now more respected and are found to be in important and responsible positions all over America. We are also given equal status and are no longer being judged by the colour of our skin.

In America now, segregation seems a thing of the past written in America's History books, although, I must say that the path to this was not at all smooth. Although, I think that very important moves have been made in America to fulfil Martin Luther King's dream, I also think that his dream was not meant to be related only to America. In my view it was for Black people all over the world. I will therefore turn my attention to looking at King's dream and relating it to Britain.

I feel that in Britain, some of the changes that have taken place are not as prominent as in America. In his dream Martin says that, "one day every valley shall be exalted, every hill and mountain shall be made low, the rough places will be made straight, and the glory of the Lord shall be revealed, and all flesh shall see it together".

In Britain today Martin's dream has partly been fulfilled because we can now find Black people in important jobs, for example we have Black members in Parliament, and many other important roles.

There have also been attempts made in some other areas of life. I do think though, it has been a much slower process here in Britain, as there are still large amounts of segregation and hidden racism being practised. Segregation is still used by some people as a dangerous weapon; that's why I think significant steps should be made to end the type of racism which is to be seen in the social economic affairs and in major institutions in this country. Unemployment, housing shortage, legal discrimination are still causes of frustration and anger among Black people .

I still think that racism is practised daily in Britain. People think that this is to be seen only in street violence but this is not so. It is to be seen in all areas of life, I believe that this makes Black people feel powerless.

No one can deny the fact that here in Britain there are clubs from which Black people are excluded; no one can deny the racist attitude shown by the media where Black people are seen to be a problem or not visible. I am not surprised then that Black people feel frustrated and not part of our society.

As a young girl living in Britain these are exactly as I see things. In my opinion, racism is a wasting social disease which comes from people who know nothing about Black people, but only think they do.

Martin Luther King was a great man who fought for what he believed in. He was a very prestigious man with a high profile. There were white people who were willing to give Black people a chance, but it was very easy to notice that all those in high society or those who had plenty, would just stick their noses in the air and go on like they did not care. It was obvious that they would love Black people to be at their beck and call or even be the underdogs of society.

I also feel strongly about the situation in South Africa and it is obvious that no attempts have been made to fulfil any aspect of King's dream there. The year now is 1989 and still people are trying to fulfil King's dream. This would almost be achieved in Britain when we have a society which accepts that Britain is a multi-racial society, where the different people and cultures are respected.

RAYMOND ENISUOH
2nd Place • Essays
Age 14

THE ROLE OF THE BLACK CHURCH

The Black church in Britain must be seen as an institution that encourages their people to go for their freedom now, and not to wait for the 'pie in the sky' after death. As shown by the Honourable Marcus Garvey the preachers and deacons must put their teachings into reality and set the wheels of the Black race moving once again. Behind all the divine words, must be divine production. As Jesus said through his Apostle James "faith without works is dead" (James 2:26). We have had many Black ministers who have done the preaching, now we need those who are able to do the work.

If all of the great preachers can inspire people to go and see Billy Graham at Wembley Arena, then they can also inspire Blacks to build supermarkets, and houses. When successful Blacks obtain wealth instead of spending it on the community they buy Porsches or HI-Fi's. The Black church must teach these people about their role and responsibility towards their brothers and sisters.

To stop the evils of racism and prejudice the Black race must command respect, and the only way to do this is for the community as a whole to become more organised, employed and wealthy. Black parents must also give their children high esteem and pride, and educate them on the worthiness of being Black. Too often children make fun of their friends' African characteristics such us calling them 'big lips' and referring to their hair texture and shade of skin colour. This must be eliminated at once.

5

Unity is also a must. It is impossible for the Black race to progress if they are incapable of working compatibly with each other. As the old trade union saying goes "Together we are strong. Divided we fall." But co-operation can only come if we clean up our morality. The pimps, drug pushers and criminals must be taken care of by us, and not the police who will look the other way if offered a suitable price. Black people must respect each other and each other's property. There is nothing worse than having been robbbed by our own flesh and blood. This is indeed a terrible crime and culprits must be dealt with accordingly.

Many Black children commit suicide after seeing the hopelessness and depravity, of being coloured in a white man's land and where whites control the world. The only way to stop this is for the church to come forward and show the youth that life can be wonderful, and that there is a reason for existing. The youth must be the nucleus and movement for Black advancement. They must forget about the past and look forward to a Black future. Then when they have children they shall educate them in Black pride and soon all the generations will be, as James Brown would put it 'Black and proud".

In the 1920s the Honourable Marcus Garvey, started a new movement, the Universal Negro Improvement Association. The movement encouraged the use of black run companies such as the Black Star Line, shipping company. Now this is what we must do to further our race. Marcus Garvey is dead but his concepts and ideas live on. The Asians have recognised the importance of controlling production before us. In almost every area where Asians live there will most probably be a corner shop or greengrocer's, either Asian run and/or funded.

Once again our race has become last to the finish line, but with production behind us through the churches we will be unstoppable, and no race will ever be able to exploit us again.

OLIVIA O'CONNOR
3rd Place • Essays
Age 10 -15

MARTIN LUTHER KING'S DREAM

There was a Black American Baptist minister who was the main leader of the Civil Rights movement in the United States in the 1950s and 60s. His name was Martin Luther King. Mr. King was born on January 15th 1929 in Atlanta Georgia and he was the winner of the Noble Peace Prize in 1964.

'I have a dream; I say to you today my friend even though we face the difficulties of today and tomorrow, I still have a dream. It is a dream deeply rooted in the American dream.' It all started with Rosa Lee Parks, who was tired and wouldn't give up her front seat for a white person on the bus. This was against the law! What sort of law was that? And is it still that way today?

If you asked a person if they were prejudiced or racist they wouldn't admit to it! No one would admit to it, but everybody had their little hang-ups whether it be about race, religion or just the way you look. But in those days, it was common practice not to have any feelings whatsoever, for the Black people.

' I have a dream that my four little children will one day live in a nation where they will not be judged by the colour of their skin, but by the content of their character.' People are still judged by the colour of their skin for example in schools. Although it is not always the case, teachers may pick on a pupil because s/he is Black. They have four words

7

programmed into their minds which are, 'I hate Black people.'

Many cases have been heard of but one springs back to mind. A white girl said to a few Black people that Black people should be kept in cages. The Black children ganged up against her. When she told her parents they came down to the school to complain. So the parents agreed with what their child had said.

Most people become racist as a result of an impression made on them at a young age. You should be judged by your character, the way you act and most of the time we are not.

If America is to become a great nation this must become true. Is America a great nation or is England a great nation for that matter? Black and whites are still separated a bit. I think some of it is that, Black people are not willing to forgive and forget. Although it is not all that easy to do. I think that if people would try a little harder we'd be halfway there.

Racism is a problem, we are all subjected to it at some time, some more so than others. Martin Luther King just gave Black people the push to get up and do something about what was being done to them. I think his dream has been fulfilled to a point where there has been a little give and a little take but the barrier is still there standing strong. The barrier between Black and white people is like the Great Wall of China. It is old, it stretches far and wide and is still standing tall and proud. There are some small holes in this wall for example letting Black people into politics and more important jobs.

Racism was beginning to become a thing of the past but it could only take one person to start it off again. Then it will spread like the 'plague' again. Mr. King's dream has gone far in development, but still has so far to go. It is so near and yet so far away from being fulfilled. Black people have been through a lot and deserve to be treated like equals not the 'underdogs' of the world.

If some white people heard or even read Mr. King's speech, it would start them thinking and maybe, they might even feel guilty. Even if we were all the same, the world would be a pretty boring place. Everywhere you went there would be a carbon copy of yourself. There is a lot of work which has to be done to make other people realize - we have feelings as well.

"We will be able to speed up that day when all of God's children, Blackmen and whitemen, Jews and Gentiles, Protestants and Catholics will be able to join hands and sing in the words of the old Negro spiritual "Free at last! Thank God Almighty, we are free at last". When Mr. King was shot and killed in April 1968 by James Earl Ray, was it the end of the beginning or was it just the beginning of his dream?

MICHELLE MATTY
Commendation • Essays
Age 10

SCHOOL CAN SOMETIMES BE UNFAIR

My mum is white and my dad is Black. They are from different cultures, that means I am half caste or mixed race. To some people that's wrong. They find it harder to accept half-caste people more than they do Black, Asian or Irish people. At one time Black and white people were forbidden to mix. Just the thought of Black and white people having a half-caste baby was unthinkable for some.

In some schools Black children would not be allowed in, and if somehow, they did get in; white children and their parents would make sure something was done to get them out, and keep them out, whether it made them unhappy or not. Today if children get into fights in school often the colour of their skin comes into it, and also the colour of their parent's skin and how they don't mix. I've been there, I know how it feels to be jeered at just because you happen to be a different colour.

I often wonder where I fit in, where I belong, can you tell me? Will half-caste people, Blacks, Irish, Asians ever fit in? Will we be treated like everyone else? In some shops the people serving may refuse to serve you and you may have to leave the shop empty-handed. You get called names like half-breed and half-cooked. What do they think we are, some kind of animal? I can remember my sister just saying the other day how her so called friend said something which made her angry she said, "Oh yeah, you're half-breed aren't you?" My sister said she felt like punching her there and then but she was a friend so it didn't feel right even though it hurt.

10

I suppose in every school you go to there is racism and prejudice. In my school we have two Black teachers and nine white teachers, not that that means anything. It just goes to show that there are more white people in good jobs here than Black people. I hate feeling that I am hated and resented by people. I am proud to be what I am, I am proud of my Mum and Dad and their colour and the fact that their families originated from Africa. I have no reason not to be proud and neither do they.

The only real reason for some people not liking us is the colour of our skin and where we come from. People treat half-caste people like nobodies with no ambition. But we'll show them won't we ?

WINNING ESSAYS
AGE 16-19

SHEILA EZENAGU
1st Place • Essays
Age 16-19

THE BLACK CONTRIBUTION TO WHITE CULTURE

"What sort of country will Britain be when its capital, other cities and areas of England consist of a population of which at least one third is of African and Asian descent? My answer....is that it will be a Britain unimaginably wracked by dissension and violent disorder, not recognisable as the same nation as it has been, or perhaps as a nation at all."   *(J. ENOCH POWELL, BIRKENHEAD, 1985)*

It's like we're all turned out the same in Balsall Heath. There's no racial fuckeries round this way! Its like.............I know there's no such thing as England any more...................Welcome to India brothers! This is the Caribbean! Nigeria!...............There is no 'England" man!...............when will they wake up? This is the new world man, this is what is coming.
                    (JO JO, BALSALL HEATH, BIRMINGHAM, 1983)

One of the most profound cultural changes that has occurred in British society over the last twenty five years has been the impact of Jamaican popular music on the young white population. But what does it actually mean to young whites themselves to have grown up in an urban area, sharing the same streets, neighbourhoods, schools and youth clubs, with Black people? What is it like to be attracted to Black culture and music? What kind of experiences and identities have these processes generated?

Perhaps it is time to open up the relatively neglected question of white (English Irish, Scottish) Cypriot, (Turkish and Greek) and Asian responses to Black people, (African and West Indian) and Black cultural forms. An exploration of some of the broader ramifications of sustained dialogue and contact between Black and white Britons in inner cities could be 'sighted' challenged and debated.

The time is roughly 2 a.m. during the indefinable zone, Saturday night and Sunday morning. The Birmingham suburb of Northfield has shut down, its pubs closed many hours ago, and most of its inhabitants long since returned to their beds - most, but not all. For in a dilapidated block of flats behind the giant Longbridge car plant, something is going on. Life is stirring and people moving to a particular kind of rhythm, with a different sense of time to that embodied by the adjacent monolith to British motoring. Tonight, Scientist Hi-Powa, champion sound system of South Birmingham, are playing a musical meltdown, as it says on the ticket to which 'all posses are welcome.'

Approaching the flats on foot, the faint reverberations of a bass line can be felt several blocks away, carrying through the buildings and along the pavement. As we enter through a broken down doorway, the DJ's voice becomes audible above the now rumbling bass patterns. Moving swiftly up the stairs, we knock on the door, greet the gateman and enter...

The session is 'ram' tonight, the atmosphere hot. Squeezing past the tightly packed bodies, the crowd seems especially young. All posses are indeed present, for the balance between black and white, and male and female, is strikingly even. The blues' young patrons intermingle freely with one another, dancing and talking, joking and smoking.

Demon, the MC, sends out big 'requests' and 'special dedications' from the mike to all sections of the crowd, drawing them in, promoting 'strictly niceness', fostering a sense of togetherness. Played by-the-champion-sound-in-the-whole-wide-world' he exclaims in one rapid breath, introducing a new selection; 'musical ting-like-the '-Rambo' -by-the-cat-called-Super Black. The needle drops. On hearing the familiar intro, two white girls standing by the speakers in smart evening dress, handbags over shoulders and cigarettes in hand, begin to sway to the rhythm...........'Haul and pull it mi selector.' As the needle is brought down on the dub, the excitement moves up a notch. Shorty takes up the mike and begins to chat...........

England today is the homeland of many people. Different kinds of people including Black people. These Black people may label themselves, African Black, West Indian Black, Afro-Caribbean, Black British and so on. However, what is of significance is that like other people these younger generations of Blacks, unlike their parents, can be two things or maybe more correctly stem from two belongings, their Britishness, and as in my own case, their African origin. So what is the net result here then, one may ask? The result is crystal clear. Unless the person in question 'shames' herself to the fullest, the derivation is simply the benefit of the best from both cultures. An outsider, yet, a member.

There now exists a substantial and growing body of research into Afro-Caribbean cultures (that is the culture of West Indian people), to confirm that Afro-Caribbean people did not 'lose' their African cultural heritage, but retained important elements of it in their language, religion, political philosphies and particularly their music. Contrary to this it must be added however, that equally while retaining what was originally their own, the West Indian people created and adapted to a culture which was 'pure' Afro Caribbean.

A British citizen of African origin whilst taking note of the 'sameness' of her West Indian peers could equally remain an outsider to this 'pure' Afro- Caribbean culture whilst at the same time claim a conscious right of direct access. A new situation emerges for this benefactor of both cultures, a discreet, but an aware introduction to a 'third' culture.

The appropriation of Black styles of dress and dance is by now a well acknowledged and established feature of white youth culture, with numerous historical precedents. Styles of dress and appearance have long had a particular extensive impact on white youth. For example in Birmingham, as in most major urban areas with large Black communities, the influence of Black styles was commonplace, and sufficiently widespread as to be detectable amongst suburban young whites who had little or no contact with young Blacks. Indeed, Black styles of dress had acquired such a common currency amongst the young generally, that it was often difficult to ascertain the precise cultural derivation and symbolic meaning of individual items.

The vast majority of young whites undertook a highly selective appropriation of Black styles, displaying only minor indications of Black influences, for example, a skirt here, or a jacket there. The specific forms that these influences took, moreover, were continually changing in tune with the ever turning cycles of youth fashion. Thus, by the mid-80s the styles associated with reggae culture and the 'roots' look of Rastafari had already become somewhat outmoded, and were being rapidly replaced by new styles associated, with funk and hip-hop culture such as 'curly perm' hair styles, hooded anoraks, sports wear and casual 'designer 'clothes.

Style, then, was only one dimension of youthful white involvement in Black culture from which little could be deduced about the nature and meaning of that involvement. A more telling and concrete register of Black culture's impact on young whites was the adoption of speech patterns (Hewitt 1986). Hewitt found that the acqustion of Creole by some young whites occurred almost involuntarily in school and street contexts, its usage growing and developing alongside that of their Black peers. By their mid-teens, Patois was being used unselfconsciously by those with a high proportion of Black friends as part of their normal conversations and peer group banter with young Blacks. Hewitt found that the levels of use of Creole by young whites varied from the use of odd words and phrases for full blooded usage as fluent as that of young Blacks.

The form and contexts of such usage followed familiar Afro-Caribbean patterns. Patois could thus, be variously used as a means of conveying specific tones and emotions such as sarcasm, joy, anger, irony, humour and drama in association with questions of competition, prestige and personal excellence, in reference to the opposite sex or perhaps more commonly, as a form of abuse.

Such use however, did not automatically signal friendship from the young Blacks towards the whites. It was required to rest on close, pre-established ties if it was not to result in harsh condemnation from young Blacks. Indeed, imitation and insensitive or jocular use of Creole could be as much a means of identifying with Black friends as a way of conveying or displaying racist attitudes towards them.

While Patois functioned as a cultural mediator of Black and white interaction, it was also used by young whites in contexts from which Blacks were largely absent. With its high prestige and 'street credibility', Patois could be employed in all-white company for display purposes or as a mark of difference from white peers uninitiated in Black culture. In this way these whites could themselves become transmitters of Black speech influences to those who had little or no contact with young Blacks.

The association of Patois with conflict and assertiveness in Black usage, made it particularly amenable to use in an oppositional mode by young whites. Nowhere was this more apparent than in the school context where white usage often paralleled that of young Blacks. As a vehicle of resistance and an emblem of cultural difference, Patois could be used to exclude and confound authoritarian figures such as teachers.

"It was a history 'O' level class, and there weren't any Black kids in that class and this teacher, right, I kept swearing and cussing him down and arguing all the time in Patois. He couldn't understand it like (laughs) and he'd be really mad, and he'd say like "stop mumbling, stop that mumbo jumbo" and all this.   *(Shorty, Balsall Heath Birmingham)*

However," I accuse the young Blacks in this country, in fact, I accuse Jamaican Blacks (doesn't specify whether these Blacks are male, female or both) of lacking the courage of 18th century slaves...Today in conditions far removed from slavery, we have Black youth surrendering in despair and finding occupation in meaningless things such as reggae and the Rasta cult. You are a failure because you are a failure at school.

At school instead of making a great effort like the Africans and Asians, you allow the pains of past and present prejudice to destroy you, rejecting education which is so important in this world. You find consolation in the words and songs from Jah, but this is Britain....At school you could have made a gallant effort to absorb English, Maths, History, Art etc...But no, shaking your backside at discos and at the entrance of record shops was of greater importance..."

What does the future hold in England I always ask myself, a new England? Who knows? It's like, I love this place.. there's no place like home. Balsall Heath is the centre of the melting pot, man, 'cos all I ever see when I go out is half Arab, half Pakistani, half Jamaican, half Scottish, half Irish. I know 'cos I am half Scottish-Irish.

Who am I? Tell me. Who do I belong to? They criticise me, the good old England. All right then, where do I belong?...You know, I was brought up with Blacks, Pakistanis, Africans, Asians everything, you name it.......Who do I belong to? I'm just a broad person. The earth is more. You know, "We was not born in England. We was not born in Jamaica ....We was born here, man! It's our right!" That's the way I see it...That's the way I deal with it.

BIBLIOGRAPHY:-
Newspapers
Rastafarianism and the Black Youth
Black Culture, White Youth

BERNADETTE FRANCIS
2rd Place • Essays
Age 16-19

MARTIN LUTHER KING'S FAMOUS DREAM SPEECH

To know if Martin Luther King's dream has been fulfilled (in part or full) you must first know of the famous Dream Speech, which was voiced to millions of people in1963 at the Lincoln Memorial for the Negro Civil Rights Movement.

Martin Luther King was striving to bring Black people to their rightful place in society, where they could be proud of who they are, what they are, and to get the ruling white majority to show them the same respect they would show their own. It was his dream that human beings would be able to live in peace, regardless of their colour and class status. To know if his dream has been fulfilled it would be best to break down the 'dream' speech into parts. Martin Luther King had six things voiced in his dream.

1. He knew that Black people had difficulties to face today and tomorrow.
2. For people to understand that all men were created as equal.
3. That slave and slave owners will be able to live in peace.
4. That the state of Mississippi will be transformed into a state of freedom and justice.
5. That people will be judged by what comes within them, and not the colour of their skin.

21

6. And that all men could join hands and rejoice at being free.

If we take point one. We can see around the world the struggle by Black people to be free in a world they helped form. I think Martin Luther King could see that Black people, before being totally accepted, would have to go through a lot more suffering. Black people are still seen as a threat, and people have a tendency to always expect the worst from them. Until that wariness of us can be expelled, until we can be seen as total human beings who experience the same emotional needs as white people, until it is realised that the only difference between us is the colour of our skin and nothing else, then the struggle has to continue.

The second point of the 'dream' that Martin Luther King wanted to see is 'that one day this nation will rise up and live out the true meaning of its creed. We hold these truths to be self-evident, that all men are created equal.' Black people are not seen as equals, they never have been. We are still classed as lower class citizens who have just come off a banana boat.

Many people will think that a lot of the white people no longer see Black people in that way, else why would there be Black MPs and Black Mayors. But it is not because they see us as equals. If they do not let a few Black people have prestigious ranks, then they know that we would rebel. For if you have no power to use then you fight for it as you have nothing to lose. But when you've got a little power then you want to nourish it and acquire some more. So that's why you have a few Black people in power.

His next hope was "I have a dream that one day on the red hill of Georgia the sons of former slaves and the sons of former slave owners will be able to sit down together, at the table of brotherhood". Slavery is something that is so deep rooted. I'm not sure that it can be forgotten. The persecution of so many innocent people is something that can never be forgiven. You can try to understand but can you honestly say you can forgive? You must understand that even though slavery was abolished in 1863, the suffering of Black people still goes on. And I don't think that

22

the forgiveness can be bestowed just like that. It's going to take a long time yet.

"I have a dream that one day even the state of Mississippi will be transformed into an oasis of freedom and justice." The state of Mississippi is a complex state as it bred slavery, and still has supported segregation. It seems to be getting no better. It seems to be staying in one time zone; instead of being in the 1980s, it still has the 1960s view in mind. Black people there are not granted all their litigations. The colour of their skin makes up their pursuers' minds. If they're Black then they are guilty, there is no room to consider they may be innocent or to even consider what made them commit the crimes they did.

In Mississippi Black people are still considered as the beasts of burden - to do all the dirty work. To be their servants, is the reason why slaves were brought to America. That is a deeply rooted belief. Fathers have been telling their sons, and then the sons tell their sons. And they honestly believe it is correct to treat Black people in this way.

Martin Luther King's next dream was "I have a dream that my four little children one day will live in a nation where they will not be judged by the colour of their skin but by the content of their character.?"

The colour of our skin is the only thing that separates us from other races. Instead of our colour being a blessing it seems to represent a curse. If a Black person seems to have too much, then they must have acquired it through a bad deed, which is not always the truth. If the division between skin colour still remains such a high hurdle to jump, then I can't forsee any Black person being judged for what's inside of them. They will still be judged by the colour of their skin.

The final part of Martin Luther King's dream is "When all God's children, Black men and white, Jews and Gentiles, Protestants and Catholics will be able to join hands and sing in the words of the old negro spiritual, "free at last, free at last, Great God Almighty, we are free at last."

This day has yet to come. You'll get some people who will want to achieve world peace; others will still proclaim that segregation is best, whilst the groups such as the Ku Klux Klan still preach their beliefs, and Black people have their rights taken away as in South Africa. How can Martin Luther King's dream ever come true? Instead of going forward, it seems that in some parts of the world we're going back to the days when Black people were counted for nothing. People will think that Martin Luther King lived for nothing, because all that he wanted, has not happened.

But if you go back to the beginning of the speech he talks of having to face difficulties of today and tomorrow. That doesn't mean we are going to get freedom in about two years. We're going to have to wait a long time. But we mustn't give up, for if we do, then we shall lose all that the great leader fought for. Most of all Martin Luther King's efforts would be all in vain and his dream would still remain a dream, having yet to become a reality.

Martin Luther King has been dead for 21 years. It's a pity that he strived so hard for this dream, and its realisation is still not in sight. Our march for freedom still has to go on or we might as well go back to the slavery days. It would be a waste of all our suffering and all the Black people's hardship to let it go now . It would be like signing the Black race's death warrant.

DONNALEE RICHARDS
3rd Place • Essays
Age 16-19

UNITY IS STRENGTH - FORWARD AS ONE

This piece of writing will include anything that has happened and what anyone has done or said that has influenced my life. I will explore my dreams for the future combined with what reality might bring, and the pressures which mould me from now until then.

Learning about my culture and seeing and hearing what happened to people of African descent, since before the sixteenth century until right now in modern times, has made me a more serious and mature person. Learning about my history and finding out where I came from and how my ancestors were tortured and killed has placed a tremendous influence upon me. People like Martin Luther King, Steve Biko, Nelson Mandela, Malcolm X and Marcus Garvey all fought for Black people to live life equally with white people, because since being taken from their native countries, Black people still live in slavery in officially non-racist countries, for example America and Britain.

However, there are countries which are openly, unashamedly, and officially racist, the most publicised of them being South Africa. Africa is what Black people would call 'The Motherland'. So Black people not only have to cope with their 'brethren' captured and killed, but also with the fact that this violence is in the land that produced Black people. They find it very difficult to accept that Black people are practically slaves in their own country. The way that white people have tortured and killed Black people for centuries, has moulded my personality and the way I think tremendously.

25

Pik Botha is the target of many Black people, because he encourages this violence upon the Black people of South Africa. Pik Botha is the Prime Minister of South Africa, so instead of using his power to help Black people in their campaign, he encourages apartheid and so many of the white people believe it is the right thing to do, but that is because they are ignorant.

They do not realise that Nelson Mandela has suffered, and is still suffering at their hands, and they do not realise that Steve Biko was killed while being held in prison. Winnie Mandela is one of the many who fight against the disgusting and inhuman torture given to Black men, women and children in South Africa.

In America, Martin Luther King was assassinated because of his influential superiority. That is why people who felt threatened planned and carried out his assassination. It makes me angry to hear that Black people are an obvious target for racism and that although it is very easy to commit racist actions, it is very difficult to prove it, and because of this disadvantage, Black people have suffered and will continue to suffer as long as white people control portions of this earth.

America has a 'Martin Luther King Day' and a 'Black History Month'. As these are important days which ought to be remembered, I think the decent thing to do is to make these days an international celebration so that the rest of the world is aware that Black people have progressed from the stereotypes made of them to being professors, scientists, university lecturers and have become successful in all walks of life.

Martin Luther King is the man whom I respect the most because of the way he used his influence to create unity and peace between Black and white. His style was of a peaceful nature, which earned him a Nobel Peace Prize, quite the opposite of Malcolm X whose efforts of achieving equal rights between Black and white were through violence. Both played a crucial part in the change of attitudes although their styles were completely different from each other. Martin Luther King's effort has earned him a 'Martin Luther King Day' in America.

What also makes me angry is when white people exaggerate our characteristics and culture for their entertainment. They imply that Black men only possess brawn and not brains, and they exaggerate our features, for example, broad noses and thick lips.

The thing that I pray for every night is for the unity of people of every nationality, especially white to Black, but as I say, this will never happen as long as white people consider that they control this earth. I say this because in 'Robinson Crusoe', Crusoe is stranded on an island in the middle of nowhere, and he encounters a Black man whom he rescues from certain death. In return for his life he makes the man understand that he must serve him and Crusoe is 'The Master'. This story implies that Black people are savage cannibals in their native country. Another thing is that this story is being taught to children at school at a very young age, which could contribute to them growing up with distorted minds.

That story was on a small scale because it just included the space of the island, but as I see it, Black people will forever be unofficial slaves on earth until people of all races change their attitudes. Crusoe practically brainwashed 'Man Friday' so the man lost his culture when he was able to understand Crusoe's.

This is exactly what Martin Luther King meant when he said: "Have you forgotten that once we were brought here, we were robbed of our name, robbed of our language, we lost our religion, our culture, our God, and many of us by the way we acted, we even lost our minds"

I'd say that the last line "And many of us by the way we acted we even lost our minds" was a result of what Black people were put through, and because they were tortured mentally as well as physically, it made them 'snap' and they became just as violent as white people, and that was going against King's wishes, because he wanted us to be strong, but in a non-violent way.

Public Enemy is a Rap group, who speak out at the system which gives Black people a disadvantage in the world today. They are very popular because they are serious in what they say in their music and people notice that they are serious both in person and in the quality of their lyrics. Being in the situation of speaking their mind in such matters, has caused them a lot of problems. One member of the group was banned from entering Britain when they were on tour because officials thought he was 'too dangerous'. This member joined the group because his father was murdered by the Ku Klux Klan. Another problem is that they themselves are accused of being racist because they allegedly put white people down in their lyrics and white people feel intimidated by it.

The group should not be victimised by the media and police because they speak their minds; besides, the fact that both this country and America say they believe they run free countries in which people can speak their minds. What the group say is true. A fact to prove this is that they have fans of every nationality who would not be fans if they did not agree with the message that the group tries to put across.

By being Black myself, I am sensitive to even the slightest racist taunt, and so I can detect it in a flash, but a white person would not be able to understand my sensitivity because they themselves have not grown up with these insulting remarks, and so could not possibly understand my feelings. I feel that Black people will forever face prejudice. Name-calling is something which cannot even be compared to the other things that can happen to Black people, for example, lynching.

The Ku Klux Klan also place an effect on my life. These people have a warped, twisted and distorted mind concerning Black people. They have performed some horrendous attacks on Black people, because they believe in white superiority. I cannot understand these people's reasons for continuing their senseless attacks, but I think that the original raison d'etre of the Ku Klux Klan was probably influenced by the fear that the oppressed Black people would form a resistance group and rebel against the norms expected of them in society. But nowadays the Ku Klux Klan operate in a more sinister and evil way and they indulge in violence almost for the sake of it. These people are so lowdown that they can be compared to Hitler and how his warped mind operated.

I read the books of Black writers, and from learning and understanding the situations that they have expressed in their writing, I have produced my dreams for the future. It is for the world to come together in unity and be free of greed and hate; also to be happy living in a world that isn't violent, greedy or hateful.

So with many of the Black peacemakers being killed, it seems increasingly likely that the dream that Martin Luther King and I share as a world becoming a better place will only be a world which exists in dreams.

Malcolm X once said: "I know that societies often have killed people who have helped to change those societies. And if I can, having brought any light, having exposed any meaningful truth that will help to destroy the racist cancer that is malignant in the body of America - then all of the credit is due to Allah. Only the mistakes have been mine".

Although the equality that Malcolm X believed in was right, he went the wrong way about improving the laws. The answer was not through violence, and that is why I believe that Martin Luther King's efforts turned into achievements, because he used peace. The members of campaigns which oppose apartheid are, I'm pleased to say, not all Black. The fact that people of all nationalities agree with these principles show that the world could change in the near future, and for the sake of our children and future generations, we hope and pray that this goal will be achieved.

And so to end with a text that Steve Biko himself spoke: "We are looking forward to a non-racial, just and egalitarian society in which colour, creed and race shall form no point of reference".

WINNING ESSAYS
AGE 20-30

DEIRDRE ALISON WOODS
1st Place • Essays
Age 20-30

BLACK WOMEN - IS THERE A POSITIVE ROLE MODEL?

Black women have always carried the burdens of our race as mothers, healers, nurturers, teachers and comforters from the beginning of time. In our most recent history, during slavery, the burden was even greater as Black women strived to keep the spirit of our people alive, and strong. To ask if there is a positive role model for the Black woman is both blind and narrow. Blind in not realising that as Black people in the late twentieth century, even our own images of Black women have been coloured by centuries of racism, sexism and the nineteenth century white ideology of feminism.

The white woman was elevated to the status of being the "ideal woman", possessing the feminine characteristics of submissiveness, tenderness, delicacy, warmth - of being Madonna-like, whilst the Black woman was degraded to a third class citizen; a bitch; a whore - aggressive, loud, stubborn, lustful and loose. The Black woman was not considered to be a woman but a breeder, or a servant, or field-hand but most of all an object to be used for the sexual gratification of men (including Black men). To ask this question is narrow in that Black people are not breaking free from the chains of this psychological slavery; free in order to form our own ideologies and concepts, free to set our own standards.

So what is this concept of a 'positive role model'? It cannot be easily defined in a few simple lines without first understanding 'positive', 'role', and 'model'. The use of the word 'positive' implies that there exists a 'negative'. Positivity and negativity are essentially governed by one's values of good and evil. Positiveness tends to emphasize what is good or laudable, that which is constructive. Negativeness tends to emphasize the opposite; that which is bad, destructive.

It is my understanding of 'role' to be the rules governing behaviour. A dictionary definition of 'role' states that it is the part played by a person in a particular social setting, influenced by personal expectation of what is appropriate. This definition as I understand it, describes 'role-position', as the parts we play such as wife, daughter, mother and so on. A 'model' could be defined as a standard to be imitated, or a representation of an "ideal" as it were.

Thus a 'positive role model' as I would attempt to define it is someone who represents an ideal role position governed by rules of behaviour - our values. The standard of these values are high; though free are not easily attainable ....values such as honesty, good, love, faith in God, peace and respect for life. However, a 'positive role model' as far as I see today, is someone who represents the immoral and unethical materialism of our time. These are people in positions of power or who have gained a great degree of financial success, or is just someone in the limelight and enjoys a star or superstar status.

Whose standards and values are these, where one's worth as a person is judged not by one's human values and morals but by one's material possessions? These are not our original standards and morals - since our people progressed without placing worth on gold and diamonds. Imperialism; colonialisation and slavery have taught us these.

The prevailing racist ideology, relative to Black women promotes the idea of a 'positive role model' as being beautiful, sexy and successful (financially) singers, dancers and athletes. Can one not see that the myth that all Black people are naturally good singers, dancers and athletes is being promoted by this racist ideology? This myth not only abounds in

34

the minds of white people but unfortunately in too many of our own Black minds.

When are we going to break free from these chains? When are we going to live by the standards of our own people? It is time that we stop asking these questions and act. It is time that we stop looking for heroes and heroines and promoting this unethical concept of stardom/superstardom. We are all human beings, and no man or woman is better than anyone else. We are all equal.

It can bring no good for our Black women if we, as Black people, help to promote and propagate racism and sexism by falling into the trap of believing and adopting the white man's concepts and ideologies. We once were forced to do so when we were taken from our motherland to strange lands. We no longer have to do so.

If one were to ask our young people why they want to become doctors, or lawyers, or some sort of performing artists very few would say it is to help their brothers and sisters. Very few would say it is to bring a simple smile and some laughter into people's lives, or just for their personal enjoyment. The main reason why a lot of young people seek to become professionals and so on, in the 'role-positions' of today which bring false prestige and respect is money and material gain.

So-called 'positive role models' by these standards do exist for Black women in the likes of the Diana Ross's and Sinittas and Five Stars of today. There are also the likes of Oprah Winfrey, Toni Morrison and Dianne Abbott - but not everyone possesses the charisma, character, creative talent or sheer hard-driving determination like these women who are role models governed more along the lines of strong values.

Instead of "setting up" our daughters for disillusionment and disappointment by adopting 'stars' as 'positive role models' let us look to the women who have and will always be the backbone of our race. I am referring to our own mothers, grandmothers, sisters, aunts and other female relations.

If you stop and for a while you will realise that we have learnt our most important lessons for life from these women. They taught us to love and respect. They taught us about God, faith, trust and honesty. They taught us to be kind, to share, to be good to our fellow human beings. They taught us to be proud of our colour, our heritage.

I am not saying that we cannot draw inspiration from those who have struggled against racism and sexism to make it to the top. But it is our "mothers" who influence us the most thus should be our foremost 'positive role model'.

Black women have been raped, tortured and dehumanised. Black women have been branded "seraphim", "whore" and "bitch" because of their spirited determination to survive and to build a brighter future for their children. There is no need to ask if a positive role model exists since she has always been there from the beginning.

Black woman - is there a positive role model? Yes! Yes it is, in my concept of a positive role model ... a Black person's concept of the values our people possessed long before any so-called western civilization.

VICTOR AMOKEODO
2nd Place • Essays
Age 23

THE POLITICS OF AID AND FAMINE

This essay deals with the issue of famine in the Third World and its relationship with foreign aid from the developed or industrialised countries to the Third World countries. Apart from the fact that this is one of the issues currently plaguing the international community, famine is today virtually non-existent in the industrialised countries while it is one of the prevalent features of the Third World countries; unfortunately made up of African, Caribbean and Latin American and Asian countries most of which are relatively newly-independent.

Besides the above, the important issue as concerns aid today involves aid from the developed countries (the usual donors) to the Third World countries (the usual recipients) Intra Developed Country aid (since the post-war Marshall plan) and Intra Third World aid are negligible and inconsequential.

It is pertinent to begin with the question of famine since it has a much smaller scope than, and is inextricably linked to aid. Famine, from a simplistic definition, is said to occur when the shortfall in the production of food in any region or community is so acute as to cause starvation among its inhabitants, if not mitigated. Famine has both natural and man made causes such as drought, desertification, pest invasion, warfare and industrial destruction of the environment.

As has been noted earlier, a cursory look at the international community

37

will reveal that famine on a large and continuous scale is prevalent only in the Third World countries. The situation is worse in Africa than the other areas. Famine in Latin American and Asian countries is generally as a result of inappropriate agricultural policies, vast discrepancies in income distribution in the countries, rapidly growing birth rates in the face of stagnating or declining economic growth rates and, to an extent, violent political upheavals.

The situation, however, is generally restricted to certain parts of the countries such as the "Favelados" of Brazil who appear to bear more than their fair share of the burden of Brazil's debt, the peasants in countries such as Columbia, the "boatpeople" fleeing political tensions in Vietnam, the disaster struck regions of Bangladesh.......and so on.

The situation that occurs in Africa, however, is much more chronic. Most African countries are newly independent states faced with the uphill tasks of achieving economic independence and development and nation building in spite of their diverse ethnic compositions. They have however, been largely held back from any markable progress in this direction by a large number of interrelated problems, including famine.

Probably the worst cause of famine in Africa is the endless wars and political upheavals in the Continent. Indeed, the famine and refugee problem is most acute in the war-torn areas. This is not surprising when the poor countries spend most of their meagre national income on arms and ammunition to fight wars most of which have been dragging on for decades. Besides this, the wars tend to cripple the agricultural and indeed most other sectors of the economies of these countries. The wars also create mass displacement of peoples, often leading to starvation.

Classic examples of the above cases include Ethiopia, which since 1962, has not only been waging, a civil war against secessionist Eritrea region led by the EPLF (Eritrean Peoples Liberation Front), but is at the same time involved in a war since 1976, with the neighbouring Somalia which is making a claim on the Ogaden region in Ethiopia. This has led to great death falls not only in Ethiopia, but also in Somalia. These are two of the most impoverished countries in the world. The wars in these countries have led to one of the worst refugee problems in the world today.

The situation is further compounded by the fact that both countries are also affected by harsh drought and desertification, eating into the land from the Sahara on their northern fringes. In the neighbouring Sudan, there is a religious based civil war. This combined with one of the harshest climates in the world, long periods of drought, followed by extreme floods, led to a famine causing the deaths of a quarter of a million Sudanese last year alone.

In Southern Africa, Angola has been in the throes of a civil war between the government forces and the rebel UNITA forces since independence. Neighbouring Mozambique is also involved in a civil war between the government forces and the MNR (Mozambique National Resistance) forces. Both wars have also generated some of the worst famine, starvation and refugee problems in the world today. There are also countries like Chad in Central Africa which, with its impoverished economy and largely arid land, has hardly had any period of rest from civil war. Sadly enough, it can be safely said that most of the civil wars in Africa are legacies of its colonial past since the former colonial powers demarcated it into states without consideration for its tribal and ethnic diversity.

All the above, coupled with increasing drought and desertification from the Sahara, violent and destructive rainstorms and the incessant incidences of pest invasions (especially locusts, predominantly in the West African sub-region) have contributed to the problem of famine in Africa.

With the increasing interdependence of the international community, international trade has ensured that a country can ease shortfalls in its food production. However, many of these Third World countries are too poor to buy food to supplement their inadequate production. Many rich countries and organisations have therefore been involved in supplying these needy countries with food and money in order to prevent or alleviate the condition of famine in these countries. This is the meeting point between famine and aid or foreign aid, as it is referred to in political literature. The character of today's international system is, however, such that foreign aid has a much wider scope than the mere provision of food and money for those needy countries.

Foreign aid simply defined, is the transfer of money, goods, and/or technical assistance from one donor country or organisation, to a needy recipient country. There have been different terms used to refer to the different kinds of aid obtained, but generally, foreign aid can come in the form of grants, loans, multi-lateral and bi-lateral, official and private hard and soft, long term and short term, military and technical aid, humanitarian aid, tied or untied aid.

Multilateral loans come from a joint group of state donors while bi-lateral loans are from a single donor country. Official aid is from a state or states or international organisations such as the United Nations, the International Monetary Fund (IMF) or the International Bank for Reconstruction and Development (IBRD), while private loans come from non-governmental sources. Hard loans are loan with very difficult repayment terms for example high interest rates and short period of grace. Humanitarian aid involves the donation of food to starving people. Foreign aid is said to be 'tied' when it is given, subject to a number of conditions dictated by the donor state. It is 'untied' when it has no attached conditions.

Loans from private and official sources form a large part of the aid that goes to the Third World. However, in spite of the insistence of some scholars of international relations on the contrary, it is hardly logical to call a loan a form of aid even when they have been given on very soft terms.

Official loans tend to be softer some times but they usually carry a political price too. Loans are, in fact, nothing more than the safest business deals by the donors since they would continue to get return on these loans whether the recipient country is getting prosperous or not.

The case, in fact, with most Third World countries is that they have been getting less and less prosperous in spite of the loans because of the debt problem resulting from these loans. The debt problems created by these loans have far outweighed the problems that necessitated the loans in the first place. The cumulative interests paid on the loans have far outstripped the original loans while the yet unpaid debts continue to grow due to the Third World countries' inability to pay back the loans at the originally agreed period.

How then, can we call this aid? The situation is so lucrative for the creditors that one gets the impression that they do not actually want the Third World countries to pay off all the debts as it would end this 'safe' investment of theirs. In any case, most of the Third World countries cannot pay off their debts unless a miracle happens.

Again, in reality, no aid given by a state is ever untied. There are always, at least, covert strings to any such aid even though it can be safely said that some of the aid from private sources and non-aligned international organisations, such as the United Nations or Red Cross, are given in purely humanitarian grounds with no strings attached. The chief donor states in the international community have argued that they give aid to the needy countries because they believe they have a 'moral responsibility' to do so. However, beyond the facade of this argument, one would discern that aid is nothing but one of the many tools used by developed countries to further their political and economic interests in the world.

The poorer countries have been made pawns in the ideological wars of today through foreign aid. The donors use foreign aid to exert political influence in these poor countries. For instance France has often used the

41

threat of witholding aid from Francophone African countries in order to force them to toe its political line. A case in point is during the independence of most of France's colonies in Africa when Guinea opted out of the Francophone African alliance which was a way of ensuring the post- colonial domination by France, of these former colonies. Consequently, France ceased all its bureaucratic and technical assistance to Guinea, leaving the newly independent state virtually crippled.

Again, during the Congo crisis of the 1960s, France used its influence to make the Francophone African countries take a stand which was inimical to African unity in the United Nations. Similarly, the United States aid programmes in South and Central American countries have been used to maintain these countries as its satellite states or, as the US government would put it, 'to stem the spread of communism in the free world'.

In the same vein, they have sponsored uprisings against 'dissenting' South and Central American governments as is the case of the abortive 1966 Bay of Pigs invasion of Cuba and the scandalous sponsorship of Contra rebels in Nicaragua. This trend is wide spread all over the world. The donor countries generally exert influence on the recipient countries in order to gain support in different forms for various contentious issues in international politics.

Probably one of the best examples of the notorious uses to which foreign aid is put is evident in the Ethiopia - Somali war. The pre-1976 Somalian government was supposedly a socialist one and as such attracted a lot of Soviet technical and military aid. With the 1976 radical military coup in Ethiopia, which ousted Haile Selassie, who had been in the good books of the U.S., the Soviet Union also extended its aid to Ethiopia. However, that year saw the beginning of the war between both countries.

The Soviet Union was in a dilemma as to which country to support. Somalia eventually expelled all Soviet technicians and invited U.S. aid.

Since then, Ethiopia has been fighting the war with Soviet military aid, and Somalia, with United States support. This is despite the fact that before 1976, the US was supporting Ethiopia while the Soviet Union was supporting Somalia. It is quite obvious that both super powers are not interested in whoever has the rightful claim to the Ogaden region which is being contested. All they are interested in is the furthering of their political, economic and strategic interests in this region. They have carried the cold war to the developing countries and the peoples of these countries most of whom do not even know what communism or capitalism is, are slaughtered as mere pawns fighting the wars of another people.

A lot of the so-called military aid given to Third World governments are merely used to maintain sometimes dictatorial leaders in power so that the leaders continue to toe the donors' lines. In Chile in 1973, for instance, the ITT (International Telephones and Telegraphs) and the United States government, through the CIA, masterminded the assassination of the newly elected popular socialist leader, Salvador Allende and replaced him with Pinochet, one of the worst dictators in Latin America today. The unpopular Pinochet is today maintained in power by a lot of US intelligence and support. The United States also gave some aid to such dictators as Ferdinand Marcos formerly of the Phillipines, President Doe of Liberia, Colonel Mobutu of Zaire and so on.., who agreed to play the part of stooges in the United States.

Closely linked to this is the fact that many developed countries, in order to further their economic interests give aid solely to those who provide suitable climatesfor investors from their (the donors') countries; those who allow the donor countries very easy access for the exploitation of their vital raw materials; and those who allow their markets to be used as dumping grounds for the excess goods of the donor countries. It is in the light of such practices that a former United States president once said; "It is madness for one nation to expect disinterested help from another."

The reality of the situation is that it has long been realised that the sort of aid given to the Third World countries cannot solve their present problems. Rather, the aid tends to keep them subservient to the donor countries.

It has long been realised that the only way in which the developed countries can help the Third World countries out of their present problems is by transferring relevant technology to these Third World countries. The relevance of transfer of technology as against other kinds of foreign aid is evident in the simple philosophy which says: "Give me a fish, and I will eat for one day. Teach me to fish, and I will eat forever."

The developed countries are refusing to teach the Third World countries to fish by denying them relevant technology. Indeed, it is to the benefit of the developed countries that the Third World countries remain relatively underdeveloped since they (the developed countries) would remain the dominant actors in the international community. The hardliners with the anti-transfer of technology stance have argued, with some plausibility that the Third World countries have no right to reap what they did not sow, only to end up using it against their benefactors.

If we have to accept this stand, however, the developed countries should at least cease their deception that foreign aid is merely a morally motivated magnanimous act on their part. They should make the world realise that it is often nothing but a calculated balance of options to the best political, economic and strategic interest of the donor country.

ARTHUR HAMILTON
3rd Place • Essays
Age 20-30

THE POSITION OF THE BLACK CHURCH SHOULD BE....

In this essay I would like to briefly examine the issues surrounding the present controversy concerning what the position of the Black church should be. It is indeed a controversy that spans theological, social, and political dimensions. Within these dimensions there is much disagreement concerning the position the Black church should adopt, particularly in the churches social and political context. Much of my examination will be focused on the Black church in Britain.

The Black church is, most would agree, wholly responsible for the spiritual welfare of its people. This responsibility was won by default as our fore-parents experienced overt racism and rejection from the mainstream churches in the early 1950s and 1960s. The experience of such rejection served as a powerful testimony to the necessity for the initial formation of the Black church.

With introspection, it becomes clear that the Black church has, in its message, placed so much emphasis on the spiritual essence of its members, that their social and political responsibilities within the church and indeed within their own communities are seen to be of little or no significance at all. As a result of this, many Black Christians feel it is not the responsibility of the church to get involved with "earthly things" (ie social issues, politics etc), but rather to concentrate on the "spiritual issues" like the redemption of mankind and the "saving of souls". With this approach there is a danger of the church becoming "so heavenly-minded that it is of no earthly use!"

It is impossible for the Black church to effectively affect the lives of desperate "flesh and blood" people by merely confining its interest to their spiritual welfare. If the Black church is indeed following the pattern of Jesus Christ, then it must as he did, speak out for the oppressed, the poor, the disadvantaged and the marginalised (Isaiah 61:1-3).

It is in the social and political sphere that decisions are made that affect our every-day lives. It is in this sphere that the Black church must intervene to plead the case of the disadvantaged. Surely the Bible teaches that faith unaccompained by positive action is useless? (James 2 :14-17).

In the wake of the Civil Rights movement in America in the 1950's and 1960's it was fully recognised that it was the action of a lone Black (Christian) woman who rightly refused to surrender her bus seat to a white counterpart that sparked the Black community and Black churches into action. Sadly, on the other side of the Atlantic in the 1980's we have a situation where not one single representative of the Black churches was seen to make any sizeable impact in the aftermath of the so-called Handsworth riots.

With the present unjust political systems drastically affecting our every day lives, the Black church must be prepared to adopt a stance whereby it will speak out clearly and emphatically on behalf of its people.

Inside the Black churches statistics show that the number of elderly folks within its ranks are quickly depleting, and the number of British-born Blacks quickly increasing. The Black church is therefore in desperate danger of losing its credibility with the coming generation if it continually refuses to address social and political issues that are affecting its young members and its community.

The harsh realities show that the issues that are at the forefront of Black thinking minds are in essence not of a spiritual nature at all. Unfair food distribution in so-called Third-World countries, promotion of apartheid, and closer to home mass unemployment and unjust housing arrangements for the poor are not spiritual problems. These are the kind of problems that a caring church must be prepared to address. Police liaison committees as well as probation officers must hear a voice of concern and representation from the Black church.

There are aspects of the Black church that admittedly have a positive effect on its members and community. The sense of endurance and hope that Black Christians emit is to be commended. On the opposite side of the balance the church must be careful that its hope and tolerance do not remove the emphasis that must be placed on doing one's best to affect a positive change here and now in this present world.

I sincerely hope that the immediate future of the Black church in Britain will see the church finally managing to combine its spiritual message with a strong, powerful and active social and political content.

WINNING
CREATIVE WRITING
AGE 10-15

SANDRA ANNUND
Joint 1st Place • Creative Writing
Age 13

IN THE SILENT DARKNESS

In the silent darkness, hoping every minute it will last.
I feel unable to seek the light for my eyes.

I wait, longing to find truth in this darkness.
Seeking the blood, shed by many innocent people.
And the smell of the bitter odour.

It's an unpleasant life for many people; day by day.
Some live this life through a war of unpeace,
some live a solitary life.

I seem to unfold the truth and search
for unknown problems in the dark, alone, and
unfeared by the strong unlightened feeling of myself.

I do not wish to be unleashed from the darkness,
for I am afraid of day knowing that everyone,
everywhere isn't united.
People seem unjust,
they cheat, neglect each other.
Some have no feelings, others try to conquer one another.

In this darkness,
I can find many truths,
of myself,
of other people.
They can be unfeeling;
emotional and really desperate to find the main truth.
I wish this darkness could last -
searching for the truth,
in my mother's womb
For I am the unborn child,
yet to seek the light for my eyes.
And to suffer such pain and unhappiness on this earth.

LIZZIE DZVUKE
Joint 1st Place • Creative Writing
Age 13

IN A DREAM

In a dream?
Yes, that is what it is like
in this world with hardly anyone
of my kind.
What is my kind? I ask.
My inner voice answers,
You are a minority, not a kind.
But what is that minority?
Nothing; as far as anyone else is concerned
apart from you.
You think you are important.
You are not,
Not whilst you are a minority.

How can I be a majority
so that everyone will know me, us?
You have to work for it.
But I have worked all my life;
Not the way you need it, though.
Will 'Who am I' help me?
Maybe; but who are you?
I do not know.
I thought you would tell me.
I cannot tell you;
After all I am only you
in a different form.

MARCUS CAMPBELL
2nd Place • Creative Writing
Age 14

THE PROMISED LAND

THE CHARACTERS

DELBERT JOHNSON
A stout Jamaican man, who loves his beer and traditonal food. He has quite a laid back attitude, but sometimes he gets uncontrollably angry.

MARIE JOHNSON
A tall dark attractive woman, who likes to have the last say.
She spends most of her time making sure her family looks decent Now and then she follows her instincts, which aren't that good.

JUSTIN JOHNSON
A handsome young man of 17 who loves to joke and laugh. His sister and he seem to be always arguing over the most trivial things. He has a talent for mathematics.

KISSIE JOHNSON
A small and joyous Jamaican girl, who loves any kind of food. She has a peaceful look on the world.

ABIS
An Ancient Priest

INTRODUCTION

The Johnson family are on vacation in Egypt, after Delbert won the pools. Marie thought it would be culturally beneficial to visit the "Valley of the Kings" but due to a bright idea of Marie's to go somewhere quiet, and out of the way of the tour, they found themselves lost, inside a large temple. The temple had an eerie feel, and a constant light refreshing breeze flowed through the passages, which seemed to be like an air conditioner, to cool the hot Egyptian air. The walls were covered with colour pictures and symbols. Some of these pictures resembled people and animals, wearing strange robes and masks. Justin and Kissie fell behind their parents and began to talk to themselves.

JUSTIN: Look where we is. I mean she wanted somewhere quiet, but I never think she meant somewhere this quiet *(looking around)*.
KISSIE: Don't worry, we'll find our way back soon.
JUSTIN: But what if.........
MARIE: Come on. Try and remember where we come from.
Justin kisses his teeth, stands still and crosses his arms in protest.
MARIE: Now what's wrong wid you, she said *(looking menacingly at Justin)* you didn't have to come you know.

While this is going on, Delbert has been looking around. And he thinks he recognizes a door.

DELBERT: Ma - Marie me tink me recognize dat door.
Marie turns her attention to Delbert.
MARIE: Well open it den, and let's get back to the tour.

Delbert walks boldly over to the door, and throws it open. The passage is suddenly lit with a soft yellowish glow. The door leads into a large chamber. In the centre of this chamber is an enormous golden cylinder, covered with many rows of hieroglyphics. To the left of this column is a large statue of a Pharoah, with a serious face. Below this is a man on his knees. His features resembled those of their guide, but he was wearing different clothes. These clothes were white and covered with colourful patterns, which resembled a sun. The man opened his eyes, and smiled.

ABIS : Hello my name is Abis, I have been waiting for you.
DELBERT: I am...
MARIE: We are sorry.
DELBERT: Ease up, nah woman. *(Looking sideways at Marie).* Sorry man, we wandered off...
MARIE: But we back now *(smiling)*

Delbert kisses his teeth . Everyone then enters the chamber, and look around like tourists.

KISSIE: Where are the others?
ABIS: Oh, they left five thousand years ago *(smiling even more)*
DELBERT: Listen man, since we come on a tour, you've been cracking some stupid joke, which na funny.
ABIS: I'm sorry but this is the first time we've met. And I definitely don't take people on tours. I'm a high priest of Jah, praise his name. *(raising his hands in the air)* I'm here to take you to 'The Promised Land'. I guess you won't believe me; people with European concepts wouldn't. Please follow me.
DELBERT: But stop, *(turning to Marie)* the man wann come joke wid me, then him wann tell me what to do. A wah goanne.
MARIE: Shut up nah man. You nah hear him say he is a high priest of Jah *(exaggerating Jah)*, come on Justin and Kissie follow the man.

The Johnson family follow Abis towards the column, a portal appears, and Abis disappears inside. Justin and Kissie look at each other in disbelief. As they entered the portal, they found themselves in a room. The walls covered with switches, all the same size and colour, but each had a different symbol above it.

ABIS: This way

Abis began to ascend a narrow ladder. They closely followed, into another room. This was a plain yellow colour with five cubes attached to the walls. There were two windows on the walls, each were shaped as triangles.

ABIS: This is where we will be staying for the journey.

JUSTIN: Excuse me, but where is dis 'Promised Land' and how far away is it?

ABIS: The promised Land' is in the solar system of Aphrodite, which is ruled by His Imperial Majesty King Alpha and the Queen Omega. Aphrodite is 54 light years away.

DELBERT: What kind a jargon ya two a talk about, light years and ting?

ABIS: Light years is a term used, to show how far away things are in space.

DELBERT: So why not use miles, like everyone else, or you tink you is too good.

ABIS: O.K. Aphrodite is *(pause)* thirty-two million, three hundred and twenty thousand billions miles away.

DELBERT: Cheese and rice, a who you tink me is, supaman? We'll be dead an bury before we reach. Me goanne go back to Jamaica and rest.

MARIE: Wah wrong wid yu. Yu wann go back to some dingy hut wid no food inna it. The man say him know the King Alpha and Queen Omega.

DELBERT: But the man say this place is 31 million miles away. We'll be dead before we got there, even if we go by concorde.

KISSIE: Me na waan go

JUSTIN: Me nidder.

ABIS: Wait *(everyone looks at him)*. If you stay on earth, you would be in a lot of trouble. In ten years, this world will be in confusion, there will be incurable diseases and many wars. I asked my pharoah, if I could be left, and save a family of this time, from this awful fate. And there's no worry about us dying. This ship will get us there in no time. There is food of all kinds and clothes to suit the new world.

DELBERT: You nah hear him say, there going to be incurable diseases.

MARIE: Wars

JUSTIN: Confusion

KISSIE: And food *(pause)* well me a go.

After everyone agrees to go, Abis disappears downstairs. After a short time a rumbling fills the ship, then a sensation of tremendous speed went through each person. From the triangle, they could see the Earth fall away. *Abis re- appears, and pushes forward the large switch. Five helmets appear on boxes.*

ABIS: Put these on.

Abis goes towards a box, and placed the helmet on his head.

ABIS: What ever you want, will be provided. Now I feel like a Long nap. I'd advise you to change those clothes and have some rest *(yawning)*
ABIS: Good night

Abis starts to level out, and float in the air, as if he were lying on an invisible bed. Kissie places a helmet on her head.

KISSIE: I wann a big Strawberry Ice Cream.

A friendly voice filled the room.

VOICE: A who you tink you is, ordering Strawberry Ice Cream. Dat stuff is Babylonian food. All you eat inna dis here ship is ital African food. Bwoy, me wish me could taste it . Banana, Mango, mmm .... Sweet Potato, Pumpkin, Cornmeal, Yam and more.
MARIE: Well me tink we need a balanced meal. Me tink fried dumpling, salt fish and Ackee with red country pepper.
DELBERT: Bwoy fried dumpling. I want some Mangoes to.

Four trays appeared from nowhere, suspended in the air, each laid with what Marie had stated. After eating their meal, each asked for the clothes. Four sets of clothes appeared.

58

JUSTIN: What kind of rough neck clothes are dese.

MARIE: You nah have no bit a culture inna you. I want everyone to put them on. We nah wann look strange in this Promised Land.

In a short while everyone had changed clothes, and had gone to sleep. When the ship neared 'The Promised Land', they were woken up by Abis.

ABIS: Wake up we're nearly there.

DELBERT: Shut up, my dream nuh finish yet.

MARIE: Wake up, Delbert.

DELBERT: A man can't sleep no more, with hustle, chuh.

Kissie goes over to the window.

KISSIE: Abis, is that the 'Promised Land ?'

ABIS: Yes, that is where we will spend, the rest of our eternal lives in peace and harmony.

A large colourful planet lay fixed against a background of dark velvet. The Johnson family and Abis touch down safely and head towards the entrance.

DELBERT: Me tink me goanne enjoy dis.

ABIS: You will (smiling).

They stepped out into a land covered with soft green grass, rivers, trees laden with all manners of fruit and animals young and old. Finally, ancient Egyptians walked around enjoying themselves. And now they know the Johnsons were lost in a new world, of peace.

SONYA WILSON
3rd Place • Creative Writing
Age 14

IN THE DARK - SEARCHING FOR THE TRUTH

In the dark
searching for the truth
on my hands and knees
searching,
scrambling,
for what is rightfully mine.

As I crawl on my hands and knees
far away,
I see a blur of light.
But how far is far?
and how much nearer
am I
to the truth ?

I try to stand
to walk upright and proud
but in the darkness
hands
     grab me
     push me
     poke me
feet kick me
until I land
exposed and vulnerable
but not deterred.

In the dark
I lie defenceless
nothing to protect me.
As the blood
begins to flow,
physically
I grow weak
but mentally
I grow stronger
and the light attracts me more..

I want to know
everything,
to know
why these people
treat me like this,
and why I
am defenceless against
their evil ways.

I crawl nearer to the light,
as I crawl
the blows continue
but they grow weaker,
until
the only pain I feel
is that of blinding light.

Now
I see the light
Now
I have the knowledge
only Now
can I stand proud and tall.

PRISCILLA KWATENG
Commendation • Creative Writing
Age 14

TRIBUTE TO OUR FOREPARENTS

This poem is about Black people who are remarkably respected,
whose works are never forgotten or neglected,
They are people who are greatly admired,
whose qualities are exceedingly desired.

I open this poem with Dr. Kwame Nkrumah,
The first president of the Republic of Ghana,
His works were unequivocally out of one's depth,
A man who seemed to go from strength to strength.

Another man whose great works shone,
was political realist, Booker T. Washington,
The Tuskegee Institute was just one thing he achieved,
Love from both races was what he received.

Now we come to Ida B. Wells-Barnett,
who instead of clothes, was dressed in etiquette,
she was a woman who worked independently
Tolerance, was her philosophy.

In 1916, a West Indian arrived in the USA for the first time,
To his shock, the white inhabitants thought that being black was a
crime,
Marcus Garvey, proved to have optimistic bravery,
He was one of the most prominent figures since the days of slavery.

When we mention reggae, we think of a man so great
His music captured the world at any rate,
Oh! Bob Marley how brightly your tunes shone
how brightly your tunes shone,
Your music shall go on and on.

Discrimination against Black people due to the colour of their skin,
was dealt with well by the Reverend Martin Luther King,
He supported the black people like a ship is supported by a mast,
we his people hope to fulfil his dream, "FREE AT LAST".

TAIWO AFUAGE
Commendation • Creative Writing
Age 14

A JOURNEY BACK HOME

A journey back home
to Africa
where all our ancestors
originated from.
A journey back in time
to slavery.

Where did it start?
It started with the explorer
travelling the seas
In search of precious goods
to satisfy his greedy heart.

To the Caribbean
the society that provided food
For all its people.
Oh! A beautiful place
until the explorers came
to start their game
'Get what you can and go'.

They got what they could,
despoiling the islands of
their wealth
And the people of their health.

Forcing them to work on plantations,
depriving them of their freedom.

But the invaders wanted more labour,
so they 'discovered' Africa.
Textiles and tools
were exchanged for people.
About 60 million, were sold as slaves,
Slaves because they were in bondage,
not because they were less than human.
Slaves because they were in chains,
not because they weren't God's children.
But Europe didn't stop there.

They carried on colonizing
and robbing
the world of it's wealth and beauty.
Getting richer and more greedy.
Turning their fertile agricultural land
into cash crop land.
Colonizing;
Africa, Australia
Asia and America.

Centuries later Abraham Lincoln
abolished slavery
in the North.
But not before the damage had been done,
Millions of slaves had been killed
others had to escape,
had to run.
But the South cried
"We're not satisfied
these Blacks are less
than human.

They don't deserve
their freedom"
The so-called 'people of the church said.
"God has no place in heaven
for Blacks.
Blacks have no soul."
So why must we let them go ?"

Thus, the civil war began.
The North won the war,
but Blacks were still left
 without land and poor.
The Black society
lived as sharecroppers
under oppression,
as the minority.

But a journey back home
goes beyond slavery.
To the Black men and women
who have made history
but have never been remembered.
A journey back home
goes back to the early scientists.
The first astronomers and astrologers
that lived in Egypt.

They must never be forgotten.
Because going back to our roots
gives us our identity.
And let us be,
who and what we want to be.

SABINA PADMORE
Commendation • Creative Writing
Age 15

THE DOOR IS LOCKED

The door is locked
The key is lost
my mind is blocked,
and with what cost
I've lost my face.
What is my race?
looking for my roots
In the dark - searching for the truth.

Will Black people ever be free
in South Africa and the England to be?
Are we to change the world tomorrow
in a land of hate and sorrow?
I am blind
I fall and stumble
I try so hard and act so humble
but so aloof
In the dark - searching for the truth.

My eyesight is blurred,
everything looks the same
cold and bleak
white people have no shame.

What is the answer,
does anybody know?
While you all think,
I'll search for my goal
to find my life, Black people's soul
to find my roots
by searching in the dark for the truth.

WINNING
CREATIVE WRITING
AGE 16-19

RAP ATTACK - SPEAKING TO THE BROTHER!

GOD DAMN! I'm speaking to the brother man!
But it's jammed communication breaking down.
Receiver shut off put down
Red turned on. Alarm!
Communication ban
An interference with the line
An enemy messing on my wavelength band
Pissing, messing, hissing with a subtlety
Resulting though in a great calamity.

God damn! I'm speaking to the brother man
Though he is listening
I gather he's still feasting in
his old psychology.
No change
No new metamorphology

Although he's reading the teachings
of our future days
His mind's still trapped
In the thinking of the oppressor's ways.
A mind trapped in the thinking of the white brother
is held back,
Needs the influence of the other colour.

The enemy's different
we' re just letting them take the wins.
The losses are too frequent.
We've got to think independently.

God damn! I' m speaking to the brother man
but its jammed communication breaking down.
Say brother........
Why be ashamed of your race,
your physicality.
Straighten your hair with tongs so hot and acid cream.
And all those nose jobs,
Are you yourself not tortured enough?
So you're trying to fake a familiarity
for which you have not the face.
Trying to assume an identity
for which they won't give you a place.
Sustaining their false superiorism
by fearing your own humanism.
You're cringing at their racist jokes.
But faking a laugh that nearly chokes.
Yes sir ! yes master! you say with fear.
Smile when they require, and not when you dare.

Bringing out a blindness to the insults scattered
Faking of a deafness as if nothing mattered
faint faking till one is so retarded
that one starts hating the next Black brother.

THAT'S WHY I SAY GOD DAMN
I need to speak to the brother man.
But it's jammed communication breaking down.
Receiver shut, off put down
Red turned on alarm.
An enemy messing on my wavelength band.

Hissing, messing, fussing
with a subtlety
but really truly
causing a calamity
Falsely, wrongly
driving through racism
cruelly calculating
Screwing up your history.

I need to communicate
to get his thinking straight.
No more lies.
That you just simply perpetrate
a slavery mentality
just spread out over time.
It's truly essential
So just you get off my line.
So just you leave the brother alone now........ah hah!
Yah....you leave him alone now ....ah hah!
I say get off my line, I need to get to the man
He needs my rhyme, I need to feed him my time....
So you leave him alone now 'cos
God damn! I'm speaking to the brother man
But it's jammed communication breaking down.

PATRICIA COLLY
2nd Place • Creative Writing
Age 16

MY AMBITION IS TO BE MYSELF

Marsha began eating her breakfast in a hurry. Her eyes focused on the little brother she so much loved and cared for; the little brother she was so concerned to protect. He seemed to be growing up overnight now that he had started school.

Marsha watched him sipping milk from the old enamel cup and she was shamed by the thoughts and emotions suddenly flooding through her mind and memory. He was so lovely and yet so much responsibility. Marsha touched Solomon's head and for a moment the action connected to a clear image in her mind that was an image of the past: an image of her own once big, round, dimpled face, smiling happiness over that same enamel cup. Marsha smiled with him, thinking of once being a child and once loved.

Time was passing and she had to dress her brother and take him to school. Marsha had one thing left to do. She must comb her brother's hair: black, coarse and thick hair like her father's hair had been. Reaching out, she teased Solomon's hair up gently, before letting her fingers take control over the comb. The little boy began to get restless seeing the comb in Marsha's hand. His eyes widened over the cup of milk. Marsha knew she had to handle his head delicately, otherwise she'd be in trouble. Solomon's voice pierced the air as tears began rolling down his face. Marsha tried to hush him but he kept on crying.

"Stop crying, Solomon," Marsha admonished.

He cried even more. She had no choice but to continue combing his hair. But she knew what was about to happen. Ade had heard his son crying and now there was frantic pounding on the stairs, the sounds of an angry man awoken from his sleep.

"What's going on. You nuh no mi a try fe get some sleep and all mi hear is pure crying, crying. Is what you do to de bwoy?" Ade demanded furiously. Marsha stood nervously, "Nothing, Papa."

"Well how comes de bwoy a bal all de while, you nuh no mi haffe wok nights? Mi need mi sleep in de day."

"I'm combing his hair, Papa," she mumbled.

"So does it mean you have to murder de pickney?" He was shouting now and pointing at her.

"No, Papa."

"Well, tek time wid de bwoy hair. And one more ting, if I hear any more crying, mi a come back fe you; mi talking to you Marsha so stay there kin you teeth them." Ade smiled to himself at this show of power but he left the room looking tired and frustrated. Marsha's father was a hard working man.

"Marsha, hurry up and bring de bwoy to school before he's late." She had unconsciously adapted to Ade. Marsha felt sad. It was unfair. None of her childhood memories could comfort her.

There were no peaceful moments now; no more reassuring kisses from her beloved mother; no more mother. That was the problem. Nothing could ever be the same again. Marsha hated her father's attitudes but she couldn't tell him. She was ashamed of her own feelings. She was ashamed of her father and the way he treated her and the way he spoke of his son as though there was only one child. She had been his child and she loved him then.

Looking up from her dressing of the child, Marsha noticed that the day beyond their window looked as dreary and dull as she felt. The glass was veneer like her own smile and beyond there was no bright horizon. All the days were the same. Her father blamed England, London, the climate and the times. Marsha only blamed him. Even now she felt the impatience at remembered talks of 'back home', rising up inside her. Solomon played and he gazed into the room as though she had forgotten him.

"Marsha you nuh hear what mi say? Stay there, nuh bring de bwoy to school and see what you get."

Back to the everyday reality. It was only 8.00 am and he had started to get angry with her. They knew they had a relationship in which they found each other unbearable. It was there even in the silences. Her father yelled again. She felt bitter and empty; hopeless and drained. She was the burden of his heart. She felt beaten and worn out when the flashes of anger or resentment faded. She also felt anxious about what the atmosphere was doing to the boy.

Marsha began packing her school books into her bag. She grabbed her brother and escaped from the house.

It was not difficult to pretend with Solomon and she was able to leave him feeling that he at least, looked happy. But all the way to school she felt depressed, under pressure, almost insane with misery and self-pity. She did not want to go to school, nor did she want to go home. She wanted to go to university but could not find a way to tell her father that.

It had been wonderful to go for the interview and meet all those people. She had loved being in the new area and alone. She had felt young and sure of herself and they wanted her. They believed in her. The problem was that she did not think her father would allow her to go. She would have to stay at home and look after Solomon and even though she loved him, it was not going to be enough.

Sitting in the park, she remembered the times when her mother was alive, feeling aware of how her mother had loved her, how she had felt secure and part of a normal life in those days. Her mother had taken her to the park. Her dream had a place for her children to play, grow and develop. Even Ade had been gentle in those days. There would have been a place for him in the garden. It had all changed so suddenly when Solomon was less than a year old. There had been plenty of fragrant flowers at the funeral.

Suddenly, Marsha could no longer bear the park. Everything was too difficult, heavy and memory laden, today. There were little girls in the park, girls in the paradise of a mother's love and probably with adoring fathers to admire Sunday frills and white socks. But that was the past. Now, Marsha had taken her mother's role, her mother's pain. Motherhood, without any of the pleasures and little of the pride, was imposition. She felt like screaming. Without realising, she had begun to walk back to the house. It seemed like instinct was driving her to some kind of showdown.

"Yes and what time do you call this?" said Ade in a rough voice of aggression".
"Um 12.40", Marsha answered in an unsure manner. She was nervous and afraid of her father's voice which echoed in the room.
"You not even going to school and no food no cook for a man like me who has been working all night. Put a pan on de stove."

He left the room and Marsha defiantly did the same. In her bedroom, she sat down on the bed, wondering what had happened. She was tired but no longer depressed. She was fed up with cooking as soon as she stepped through the door. It seemed like Ade was about to find that out.

Ade hadn't heard any noise in the kitchen nor did he see light gleaming on the cooker panel. He started to get angry waiting for his daughter to cook. Sometimes he could not help feeling his children had got lost in England. The son seemed sweetly simple at the moment but there had been a time when his daughter, his firstborn, had seemed like a wonderful dream. He had wanted her to be both fine and educated but she seemed only morose. She had not helped him after the death. His mind veered away from that time.

"Marsha! Marsha!" he yelled in fury.

"Yes, Papa." Marsha peeped out of the slightly opened door of her bedroom.

"What happen to de dinner?" Ade walked up the few stairs, towards Marsha's bedroom where he stumbled over the last step.

"Oh! I forgot". Marsha spoke sarcastically.

"You always forgetting. What are you thinking about? How comes lately you ah forget!"

"Nothing, Papa, just tired". She rolled her eyes upwards.

"Tired of what?" Anger began to fill his mind as he stared at her in disbelief. This was his dream. He could not bear to see her. So, they stood like fighters prepared for combat. She wanted to tell him, express her feelings about her father treating her badly, but she was in two minds.

"I'm tired of cooking dinner every evening." Marsha was shy and afraid to speak to her father, but she did it and she felt good, proud of herself.

"So what you mean to say? You don't want to do as what you are told?

"Alright"....She interrupted. "No, but I need a break. Since mother died, I've been taking all the responsibility." She felt good, letting these words out of her system.

"What responsibilities? Chou! Pickney shut up." Ade threatened to give her a backhander but he kept his cool.

"Okay, who does the cooking, ironing, washing, babysitting and so on?...." Marsha stood up to him like a big woman. She had been treated like one, doing all the chores. At the same time she felt guilty talking to her father that way.

"Don't talk to me like that. I am your father. You must have a little respect. Who buy food? It's only I'n'I wok inna this place, so don't get wrenk with me, young lady. You is only 18 years of age and you could

78

be working." He was perplexed, as he took a deep breath. Marsha began to get frightened.

"Sorry, Papa, I'll cook the dinner." She prayed that he would turn back and forgive her.

"That's a good girl, I like that." Ade sadly left her bedroom. But he felt self-centred and selfish.

Ade thought about what Marsha did in the house and what he was doing. He felt his daughter needed time for herself, after all she was getting to be like her mother. Maybe his wife had died early because disease had eaten her whilst she worked for the family as a daughter and then his wife. He couldn't help wondering if his daughter would decline in the same way.

Marsha mumbled to herself. She felt like being in a prison. No freedom. Just work, work, work she thought. She hoped her brother wouldn't turn out to be the same as her father. She did not after all, go to cook for her father. There was silence in the house.

The afternoon grew into silence but this was a new silence. Ade, cooking and eating in the kitchen, felt it. Marsha, prostrate on the bed felt it. This silence swelled from their knife edge as though a wind of understanding was blowing through the house.

Marsha felt a calming of her mind and spirit. She drifted into sleep. When she awoke it was like a dream. Her father was sitting on the foot of the bed, his eyes full of the love she had forgotten but yearned for. She struggled up, "Solomon...." But her father waved a hand and she subsided.

"Your Aunt Lydia got him. You and me got to talk". And suddenly the world tipped into place and sat back on its axis. They talked and they talked. Marsha listened and understood her father's grief and confusion. She began to understand what it meant to travel from Kingston to Brixton with hopes in your heart and mind for adventures you might realise in your children.

Slowly, and with shame, she understood what her father had been suffering. He wanted only good things for her and had been afraid. He was not an educated man and he was not English. Sometimes she'd seemed very far from him as she struggled for an identity. Marsha said only two sentences as the night wore on and they were "I never meant to reject you" and "My ambition is to be myself."

By the morning she had understood many things. Most of all she had understood that her ambition would have to mean patience, tolerance and the letting go of stereotypes. She had hurt her father. She did not want to do that again.

STEFANIE TODD
3rd Place • Creative Writing
Age 17

MY AMBITION IS TO BE....

Black!
Not a
Jungle Bunny
Nigger
Darkie
Not even will I put up with
Black Immigrant!
No.

I was born here
And who says I'm as much as an ethnic minority?
There is one of me.
I am 100%
Equal majority.
I'm not even 'coloured'
I'm Black.

And when I achieve 'Blackness'
I want more!
When I achieve 'Black'
My ambition is to be
Individual.
Not a
Statistic,

Problem Area,
Grey Area;
Not even will I put up with
'One of them.'
No.

I'm one of me.
And when they pass laws about
What to
Do
With 'them',
I'm gonna stand up and shout
Oi! you forgot
Someone.
Me!

You forgot
Me!
And then I'll tell them
I'm Independent!
Not a
Rioter,
Drug Dealer,
Mistake.
Nor am I
Stupid.
An' that'll shock 'em
All of them
'SUN'
Readers.

And then I'll cry
Hey, I
(At the moment over 1/2 of the ethnic communities of Britain are British born)
Want

(Blacks have been in Britain since the first century as Roman Soldiers. That's four centuries before the Anglo-Saxon English)
To be
(If it weren't for white greed, for slavery, colonies and cheap labour, half the British non-white population wouldn't exist anyway)
Accepted!
As a
BRITISH
Citizen!
I want to be a friend of
The Police
That's my ambition.

Yeah, that's
It!
It doesn't mean
Informant
Nor does it mean
Lacky.
But you see
I don't want to be something the police have to
Tackle,
Spy on,
Ask me my business on the street at 8:30 p.m.

I want to be able
To walk up to
Coppers
With my hands
In my pockets
And stare them
Right in the eye
And ask them
Outright
The time.

Now that perhaps
To you
May seem to be asking
A lot.
But
All I really want -
My sole_
Ambition
Is to
Be
Equal.

DENA LAWRENCE
Commendation • Creative Writing
Age 16-19

I SAW IT HAPPEN

I am the wave that spilled knowledge onto
the shores of the Nile,
that surged under its people's struggles
and swelled alongside their victories.
My ripples have recorded their numerous achievements.
For when this great civilization advanced ahead of its time,
I saw it happen!

I am the palm tree that harboured the homeland
between its branches,
that buckled when the chains subjugated
the body but not the mind,
and the beat of the drum
was replaced by the clanking of irons.
For when the shouts of freedom became the whispers of bondage,
I saw it happen!

I am the rhythm of the Mississippi that washed
away the pain,
that created the songs of emancipation
and forced the cries for justice.
For when the ghostly figures burned their crosses in the night,
I saw it happen!

I am the orphan of Soweto
who exists between the curfews.
who must speak the words of an alien language
in a voice that cannot be heard.
For when the sun was eclipsed by the shower of bullets
and lessons were taught by the graveside
I saw it happen!

I am the hope and the dream of the future
holding change within her grasp
whose blood still waters the African soil and
whose heart still beats the cracking whip
on the shores of the Mississippi.
But when these struggles are just memories and the
only cries heard are those of victory,
I WILL SEE IT HAPPEN!!!!!!

WINNING
CREATIVE WRITING
AGE 20-30

BETH CREESE
2nd Place • Creative Writing
Age 24

EQUALITY UNDER THE LAW

The court room was crowded, packed and overflowing with observers representative of all sectors of multicultural and class-less Britain. The South African government would have been proud of the selection of jurors; four Black, four white and four from the mixed coloured population.

The judge presided with an impartiality unique to British justice, shrouded in the robes of wisdom which went hand in hand with her profession. The white prosecuting counsel argued and attacked in boorish fashion, and the Black defending counsel was slick and eloquent.

The defendant stood in the dock, head bowed and penitent, answering his accusers slowly, carefully and clearly. The unanimous verdict was passed; "Guilty as charged".

A muttering went up from the crowded gallery and the girlfriend of the accused comforted his weeping mother. The judge passed sentence and ordered that the criminal be taken away. The court dutifully rose with the wise old woman, and after she had slipped off to her chambers to remove her weighty robes and to meditate on past judgments, filed noiselessly out through the various exits.

It was my job to escort the criminal from the dock to the cells beneath the court room, where he was to be held until the prison transport arrived. I watched him as he came down the steps of the dock. He looked at me, smiled weakly and shrugged his shoulders. It was as if he knew how distasteful I found my role, as if he knew it was my first day.

He looked about my age. He wore a good suit, clean shirt and a sober tie. His shoes were polished to a high finish. He was well dressed, but somehow I did not believe that these were his best clothes, or that he had made any special effort for the occasion. He looked too relaxed, too comfortable. He held up his wrists expecting handcuffs, but I took his elbow firmly and guided him to the side door which an usher was guarding. The usher told me to manacle the convict.

"What do you think they're for, eh mate?" he said good-naturedly. So I slipped one bracelet around his left wrist, the other around my right, although I didn't really see the point, as, once through this door there was only a single staircase leading down, with nowhere for him to run to - up, back to the courtroom to the police or down to the cells with the waiting warders.

We walked side by side down the steps. He was slightly taller than me, my shoulders were lower than his. The stairway was dimly lit at the top, but the harsh white lights of the cells below shone on the last two steps and filled the opening, giving the illusion that instead of going down into the darkness of the earth as we were, we were coming out into daylight. A warder, a short, stocky, grey-haired man with a smooth pink face approached. He looked at me. He looked at the convict. He looked back at me, this time more cautiously.
"Hello, you must be the new boy. My name is Burt".

I was just about to open my mouth to introduce myself when he turned his head quickly to the convict, grinned broadly and held out his hand to him.
"Vicious looking brute, eh? What did he do?"
The convict did not accept his hand. He could not. His right was manacled to my left. Burt noticed this and laughed.

90

"You can certainly tell you're new to this job, you've got the bracelets on the wrong way round. Never mind. You'll learn. He's not dangerous now anyway, now that we've taken away his hunting knives and spears. Come on. This way".

He turned and led the way to a large room. We followed the sound of his laughter, both mute, struck dumb by his error. The convict looked at me, his face red with shame and embarrassment, feeling this guilt infinitely more acutely than the guilt for which he was due to serve sentence. The muscles of my Black face went limp and my big mouth fell open. I could feel the perspiration on my forehead at the edge of my woolly hairline. I gathered some composure and was about to speak, but was again interrupted, this time by the convict, who whispered:
"Really sorry, mate, didn't know there were any of them left. I wouldn't have believed it if I hadn't seen it. I don't believe it!!"
"Don't let it worry you. Story of my life. It doesn't bother me any more, though it surprises me sometimes, like now."

My mind became full of questions and dilemmas. Did I really want to work here? Well the answer was emphatically no, but I had known that when I had taken the job. But to leave now would mean another long bout of unemployment. God knows I felt like walking out. The years I had spent quietly studying for endless exams, the times I had struggled against my peers to stay on the straight and narrow. Was there any point in anything? The convict was staring helplessly at me. I said:
"Play his game. Let him have his fun. The time will pass quicker, anyway."

Burt was filling a kettle with water. He looked round at us.
"I'm having a cup of tea, would you like one?"
"Yes please", said my convict, "no sugar".
"Well, you'd better lock him up first. Here's the keys. The cells are over there."
I gave a slight tug on the handcuffs. The convict looked at me and understood the message on my face.

"No" he said, "let's keep him and show him how we do things this side of civilisation. He'll be all right, so long as he's attached to me, won't you, Sunshine?"

I caught the faintest glimmer of a wink as he looked menacingly at me and hustled me over to one of the plastic seated chairs at the melamine table.

"That'll be all right, won't it Burt?"

"I suppose so. We make our own rules down here. I suppose He wants a cup too?"....

"Well, if you can manage it, Burt...."

"He must be thirsty after a hard morning's lying through his teeth, protesting his innocence, but he ain't fooling anyone, is he mate?"

"You can say that again", said my convict, nervously.
Burt brought the tray over.

"What did he do?...I bet.. - no let me guess....burglary?....theft?....no rape! ...They can't wait to get their filthy hands on our women.!!

I sat in silence, drinking my tea and thinking. The two men laughed and joked, but gradually my convict took less part. Burt's face got redder with mirth as his monologue ranged from the generic roots of the misdemeanours of which I had been supposedly convicted, to the tightness of my curly perm, to the quality of my sun tan.

Every word he uttered encompassed all of the racial hatred and bigotry that he, as a superior, white male had chosen to take as his heritage from the glorious days of the Empire. I began to stop feeling insulted and became more curious and bewildered. He sincerely believed what he was saying!! His rant was in full flow when the prison officers arrived.

"Hallo boys", he beamed, "We've got another Sambo for you. This is my new helper, Michael." The convict and I stood up together.

"Hello Michael" said the younger of the prison officers, looking at me.

"Do you want to hand him over, and we'll be off."

I took the key from my pocket and unlocked the manacles. Burt's smile turned into a grimace. His face resembled that of the corpse of a man who had died a horrific death. The convict and I looked at each other for a few moments and he shook my hand. "Good luck, mate", he said, and released his firm grip. Just before he went off with the prison officers he glanced over to Burt who sat very still, unable to speak. He shook his head sadly.

"Don't pay no mind to him", said the older prison officer, "he'll get over it!"

"No he won't", thought my convict as he climbed into the prison transport.

"No he won't," I whispered as the van drove away.

Burt sat in his chair, immovable, gloomily contemplating the crime he did not know he had committed for which my presence was punishment. Watching him in his desolation I took pity on him. He was suffering greatly and the wound he had gouged in my spirit began to heal over, though I knew a scar would remain to remind me of the guilt that Burt had seen in me because of the colour of my skin. I drained my cup in a gesture of finality and stood up. Burt continued to stare at me in great horror and disbelief, turning to fear. I decided to put this morning's episode far out of my mind as a first step towards creating a pleasant working atmosphere.

"Cup of tea, Burt?" I said, and went to refill the kettle. "It's certainly been a hard first morning, but I'm sure I'll get used to it. If you look in that bag over there you'll find some biscuits. My mum always sends me off with a packet when I start a new job...."

And I continued to bustle around, merrily chatting away, after my custom.

KENDRICK COURTNEY WHITAKER
3rd Place • Creative Writing
Age 23

THE DEATH OF RACISM

THE BATTLESCENE...

Swooping in for the kill these steel-coated birds of prey
blasting all, all, all in their path with a flash from a deathray.

Every populated area had been hit
and communications were down;
any chance of a counter strike had been blown.

Screams were drowned out by the sounds of death
as his chariot clattered overhead
claiming for his domain the souls, the souls, the souls of the dead.
The real enemy who had been unseen
stood revealed in life's colourscheme.

True racism was finally here
and all on earth knew they had to fear
for whether Black, white, yellow or red
humankind was the hunted trophy head.

And as tears of blood ran down the earth, the veil of foolishness
was torn away
and as if every soul on the planet was touched
one envisaged Martin's dream-day.
Realisation just before revelation.

And as the sun submerged into the planet
and the survivors hid away
a glimmer of hope lingered on
that man would fight another day.

COLOUR SCHEMES PART I

Colour schemes; red, gold and green dreams.
Red, white and blue Themes.

Toe to toe, blow for blow; an early knockdown in the first round
and we all thought it was over as the Dreamlion hit the ground
dazed by the ferocity of his opponents attack.
That lion was strong, fast, cunning, arrogant and ruthless.
He gauged and clawed and snapped while the lion in the Dream-corner
was down, determined not to let him get back into the fight.
For it was right plus might, dark against light, Black versus white,
victory insight, the Themelion's night, would the Dreamlion sleep
tonight?

The Dreamlion's fans clasped their hands
fearing the outcome of this bout,
as he absorbed blow upon blow and the blood clearly showed,
the Dream was flickering out.
As he lay on the ground after being beaten down he looked around,
gazing through blood-stained eyes at his supporters eyes,
he listened to their cries and the Themelion's cries promising them a
Theme more worthy than the Dream that they so idolized.

Confident of his victory he failed to see the Dream arise.
Strengthened by his supporters' lamentation.
As they squared off for the next confrontation, more that a battle
of nation against nation. They looked into each others eyes to
see which one would claim the prize.

They were the same yet different, one driven by a Dream
the other by a Theme, a variation of a Dream.
Colour schemes; red, gold and green Dreams,
Red, white and blue Themes.

COLOUR SCHEMES PART II - THE GREEN

From outer space they watched as the conflicts raged on.
The 1st world against the 3rd, the capitalist versus the communist,
America against the Arab, Arab against Jew, to name but a few.
From outer space they watched unseen planning the entrance of the
green.

If Black and white is an issue to fight,
then for sure the entrance must be bloody.
If success for one continent is at the expense of another,
then the idea of another planet in the game will not come over.

WARLORD, I disagree as a more advanced race
we have a duty to make Earth a better place
and teach them a lesson in humility
and thereby keep our own dignity.

GOOD MINISTER, will you never learn
where there is smoke a fireburns,
we've observed Earth for a millenium
and they still can't evolve above barbarians.
They call those petty squabbles world wars,
but they are just inconsequential bores.
Let us not cloak our presence anymore
and show them the real definition of war.
Let all in favour press their council vote for green
and so begin the galactic colourscheme.

COLOUR SCHEMES PART III - THE RAINBOW

Underground in dank secrecy
met the freedom-fighters hierarchy.
The Lion, the Tiger, the Eagle and the Bear,
the Lion and the Dragon in the chair.

We must combine our strengths to snatch victory from the Green
if man is ever to walk the Earth supreme.
They defeated our armies, destroyed our economies,
outlawed our languages and religions
and enslaved our populations who amongst us have a vision.

The Eagle squawked first; put all your resources
at our disposal we will take on the Green
in a battle the like of which none has ever seen.
Vengeance will be ours,
no one can desecrate our star-spangled colours.

"With their technology! You will lead us only to
a swifter armageddon of tears", growled the Bear.

The Theme Lion joined the argument adding
to the confusion of the situation.

The Dragon called for order as he snorted
red fire in disgust at the gathered host.

A quiet exchange was also in motion
during all the commotion,
between the Tiger and the Dream Lion
who had conceived a plan of a fashion.

We have here the colours of the rainbow torn asunder,
it's no wonder we are going under.
The idea of this summit was to complement
each other's strengths and weaknesses,
to reconstruct the rainbow's purity and purpose,
to unite under one banner regardless of wealth or colour.
Not all can be rich in spirit, but even that is not enough,
not all can be rich in wealth for that is not enough,
only with a joining of our riches earnestly
can we hope to survive the Green tyranny.

The next time they would meet the Green on the battle field.
it would face a multi-headed Colourscheme; at last complete.

EPILOGUE...

As the setting blurred and faded in the colourscheme
I awoke to realize it had all been but a dream
A step into a twilight dimension
where I was the maker of life's invention.

On a world filled with sadness and glory
the death, the death, the death of racism had been my story.

OVERALL WINNING ENTRY

GOODBYE JOHN MBITI

THEME: The incompatibility between love and violence.

GOODBYE JOHN MBITI: The Beginning

(The stage is split in two, with a 'gulf' created between the two sides. Two different desks are mounted on raised platforms, with desk lamps attached, so that, at given times, that is the only light that reflects on stage. It is at and around these two desks that the play revolves).

KOLA: Mine is the gaze that refuses the seduction of my senses. Mine is the frustration at the confinement of this emotional prison; trapped in a world they call 'civilised'; trapped in a vortex of helpless souls, crying out for....

TINA: Help!....Help me...

KOLA: Yet hidden behind wooden masks that threaten to crack whenever the suffering soul begins, it wants to cry.....

TINA: Hold me .....please, hold me.....

KOLA: They do not want to see my tears. They must ignore my pain.... it is the civilised thing to do....

JOHN: I am an angry voice that bellows with the fury of bloodthirsty Zulu warriors whose pride has been insulted. I am the insistent raw-hide drums that pulsate with the life-blood of countless generations. I am the nimble feet whose rhythm....

SOPHIA: Dances, dances with the vibrancy of the earth itself, capturing the joy of life.

JOHN: Even when at work.

SOPHIA: Dancing, with the vibrancy of the earth itself, capturing the joy of life.

JOHN: When we make love.

SOPHIA: Dancing, with the vibrancy of the earth itself, capturing the joy of life.

KOLA: They wander all over the place, trying to forget. Each one living in a little cell; a cell none can share; a despair as sure as night-time brings darkness.

TINA: Help me! Please help me.

KOLA: They lie in gutters, relics of the past and this present generation. They are the visible scapegoats of society, our yardstick of decency.

TINA: The visible scapegoats of society, our yardstick of decency.

KOLA: They are in our prisons, trapped in a sea of contempt, and flooded by a deluge of society's wrath.

TINA: The visible scapegoats of society, our yardstick of decency.

KOLA: Trapped within padded cells, driven mad by the pressures of their existence... insanely singing the lullabies for their souls.... the relics of the past and this present generation....

TINA: The visible scapegoats of society, our yardstick of decency.

(Kola climbs onto the platform and sits behind his desk. Thoughtfully. He is disturbed). Fragmented dreams. Time passes. Each day screams....fragmented dreams!!.... Fragmented dreams.... you do not want to know.....you do not want to see....

KOLA: Dear John

How are you? Time flies. How long was it since the competition? Nine months? Ten months? It was a victory! A tribute to artistic skill, yours and mine. I can still hear the war cry of your Zulu ancestors as they bellow with rage at this rape of your lives and your land.

I have started working on another piece. Its grand design is in the form of an African epic. I love the rhythm in African verse. This will make people sit up and take notice. Tina is out there asking the sort of questions that people would rather ignore. I'm beginning to think she's disturbed. But she seems to need me. I'm not sure I want to be needed. She desires something else, something stronger......Compassion? Desire?

Affection? Whatever it is, I cannot define it. Thus I cannot give it; nor am I sure that I want to...

TINA: Fragmented dreams! Each day screams! Fragmented dreams!

KOLA: She takes care of me. That's important. An artist needs comfort. Comfort is essential to creativity.... *(Getting agitated affected by Tina's insistent voice)* ... artists serve a functional purpose! They cannot be distracted by the vagaries of life! We are important! The people's voice!.

TINA: Fragmented dreams!

KOLA: Closest to God....if there is a God.....drawing inspiration...we are important...even if we have scuffed shoes that don't stay clean.

TINA: Screams.

KOLA: My typewriter no longer provides the needed sanctuary I demand of it. Lust requires I answer a call, or I will sleep alone tonight. London is a cold city. It's not a place for lonely men....

TINA: Kola!!!

KOLA: Passion calls. Write soon. K.

JOHN: *(John behind desk. Table lamp switches on. Starts to read)*

Dear Kola, The dead are getting younger. But how young is young these days my friend? Our men mature at eight and die if they are lucky at fourteen. Apartheid feeds on our young. It gorges on young flesh, no longer satiated with ageing meat. Drunk with fresh, young blood, it totters surely at the brink of total destruction.

Breathless, I look on, a tiny ant....No! More irritating.... more of a discomfort...a painful boil, swelling with the malignancy of too many battered souls and spirits; swelling with the dark moon of hate that knows no appeasement; swelling with the thunderous silence of teenage pain! Swelling! Like an annoying mosquito, annoying, irritating, allowing no rest.

Do you sometimes wonder at the fate of painful boils though? Big troublesome boils? A surgical blade. Or a disinfected pin. Then the malignancy drains out in a rush. Impotent fury stifled in methylated swabs. But how many boils can you disinfect at once? A thousand? On one body? A hundred thousand? Please excuse my rambling on. But you must agree, there is poetry in death, and pain, and tears; poetry when

103

a mother heaves with a pain so deep it scars for life but she wipes her tears and bellows the "Shosholoza" defiantly at an indifferent sky. This anger is healthy. It has wakened my muse. Yours, John.

SITUATION
(Kola is at his desk, and he's writing again. Tina paces around the room for a while looking like a caged lioness).

KOLA: They are everywhere I turn. Eyes like burning coal. Footsteps that thunder, heavy with malevolence; pregnant with spoil; soaked with the sweat of my brow; gluttons, gorging on my flesh! Gorging on my flesh! Poisoned flesh! Poisoned by the end products of their greed! They lock me up in a cage of fear; fear of the tax-man; fear of the social worker; fear of the bank; a fear of debt; a fear of working the rest of my life on another man's dream.... a fear of a blade........my beard would be the only souvenir of my manhood!
TINA: I suppose you want applause?
KOLA: It would be insignificant.
TINA: It would be insignificant. Why is it that every time you get behind a typewriter, you become a bastard?
KOLA: Poisoned flesh... poisoned by the end products of their greed.... No! It's not original enough! John can think of better lines than that!
TINA: You don't really care do you?
KOLA: Eyes like burning coal.... that's a good one.... John will like that .....burning coal....There is a mad rush to kill their brains....the young generation....the new race...dirty. Jobless. Futureless. Eyes of burning coal...seeking escape...jumping between the pages of Playboy and Penthouse. Planting seed for rape and perversions. Sex. Cigarettes. Lager and drugs. The future is bright.

(Tina leaves....Kola pretends not to see her go. Then he gets up, circles his table, ensures she's gone and then rushes back to his table to fit paper in the machine. Then he starts to read. John with a desk and chair as the most prominent pieces of furniture in his part of his stage sits back and reads Kola's letter as it echoes on stage).

Dear John,
There is a rage burning deep inside of me. Deep. Deep. I cannot touch it. I cannot examine it. I cannot see it. Therefore, I have failed to determine the reason for it being there. I am afraid that its flames will engulf me. Yet, it gives such strength! Everytime I feel it, I find to my discomfort that I have developed an erection. This anger boils suddenly welling up inside me, and threatens to spew forth a torrent of obscenities into the heavens. It makes hurting those closest to me a pleasureable pastime.

I have asked myself: What is the cause of this rage? I do not know, what sparked it off this time? My scuffed collars. My dirty and scuffed cuffs. Dusty shoes, battered shoes. Aching feet and hollow belly. But certainly not a news report about a woman who spends over £500 a week to feed her cats.

Tina just left. I won this round. Who will win the next? I dread the answer. She's hurt. Badly. I know. Tina doesn't hurt easy. She's strong. She's strong. Sometimes, that worries me. A woman has no right to be that strong. Today, she just left. Perhaps she won't return. What would I do then? Find another Tina? There are too many Tinas in London to worry about the fate of one. I've got to go. I am hungry. I think I'll raid Tina's piggy-bank. Buy some chips. You just keep hurting those bastards. Keep their backsides black and blue.
You know who. K.

Dear Kola,
There is nothing wrong with anger. It is possible to table a series of literary discourses on the phenomenon of the emotion. I am only happy that I can fuel it into my work. Sophia and I understand anger. We understand when sometimes, a little spills into our relationship. You can't use coal without blackening your fingers. And yet coal provides warmth, and fire for food. There's a unique relationship between opposites which I do understand, not try to understand. Why must you?
John.

Dear John,

You must understand me. I am searching for answers. I am...we are all trapped within a complicated game, and we've forgotten the rules! I must search for those rules! I feel that deeply. I must search. This is why I was born. This is why, I am, now, at this period in time. I am a piece in a jigsaw puzzle, and I cannot find peace until I know where and how I fit. In order to help solve the problems my country faces now, I must define what piece I am, and how I fit.

K.

My Dear Kola,

We must all go through that void. That emotional vacuum, within which our roles are defined. Master or slave. Creator or critic. Man or boy. It's our period of initiation. Our weaning from the fleeting and childish pleasures of youth. Now we are men. With turgid muscles. Taut. Straining. Minds clear. Like spring water. Founts of inspiration. Pregnant. In labour! Bursting forth like a dam contained too long! Washing away the grime of centuries! Quickening spirits! Strengthening the weak! Applauding the strong!

This is why you were born. You know who you are. You know what function you must perform. Ignore the people. You have a higher vocation. A noble vocation. Quickened!

John.

My Friend,

I cannot ignore this John. I cannot ignore the pain these people feel, and have been taught to hide so well. I cannot but study to see when the mask would slip to reveal what's behind the facade....these people have been taught to seek escape....in drugs...in sex....in a blind desire for material things. Yet they yearn, John. They hunger for something more. And they keep yearning. And that insatiable hunger drives them further and further to the brink of total depravity!

K.

Kola,
What about the pain of your people? What about the pain of your country? What about the pain the Black race has suffered for generations? What about that, Kola? I am talking about the rape of Africa. That's what concerns me! I don't care if they've no longer got the stomach to face crushing realities of justice! Where was the rest of the world when Africa was treated like one big safari, when missionaries and the so-called teachers, and their bullies with 'wonder' contraptions that spat death, were crated over to play the part of Zoo-keepers? You tell me! You're a writer Kola. You've got responsibilities. You have a duty to your country. Perform it.
John.

John,
What do you know about my feelings for my country? I don't have to justify myself. Too many have tried and failed by ordinary means. Coups and countercoups. A duplication of past misdeeds. A cancer that seems to spread effortlessly from one generation to the other. A cancer that blinds and hardens. A cancer that ignores the pain it inflicts, and pretends that people never had it so good. What do you know about my feelings for my country?
Kola.

Dear Kola,
I am concerned with the preservation of our culture; of our identity. Why are you more concerned with the immorality of the West? How is that your concern Kola? Your country is going through one of its most traumatic periods in its history after the civil war. You're in Europe and exploring the deplorable state of its inhabitants. If you have a dictionary my friend, look up the word 'nostalgia'.
Perhaps harsh, John.

John,
What do you know about nostalgia? About the pain of absence from a society within which I feel encapsuled; within which, despite the trauma;

107

despite the greed; despite the corruption; despite the fear; I still feel wrapped in a warm and protective womb. A womb within which I know that, despite all else, I can dance and watch as others studiously ignore what's going on around them.

I came to the West to acquire a perspective. To acquire a measuring stick with which I might compare my love for my country. And everywhere I turn, the questions come flying at me. This evil is everywhere. In different disguises. Here, it is made worse by a worsening indifference to the hurting people around them.

Do you know what my fear is John? My people look to the West. Whether they want to admit it or not. They are influenced by the West. What else are all those computers doing? Turning people into computers too? Indifferent? Blind? Insensitive? Despite everything John, my people have not forgotten how to celebrate. That is what I miss the most. That is what I criticised the most. Perhaps that was our escape. We could dance our fears away ....for a short while anyway. Too many people are hurting out here. In South Africa, you have the sympathy and support of the world. In London, nobody cares, because no-one wants to admit that there is a problem here....
Kola

Dear Kola,
You are asking questions that will drive you mad. Just like all the others who questioned. You cannot appreciate beauty without its unfortunate shadow, ugliness. You cannot take your health for granted without sick and disturbed people for you to despise and avoid like lepers. You cannot drink and stuff your nostrils with drugs, celebrating your freedom if you didn't have South Africa as a ready recipient of your syrupy sympathy, and your loud gestures of support! You're getting involved Kola. You're getting involved. Perhaps it's time you went home.
John.

SITUATION
(Kola's boiling. There's a long silence before Tina speaks).

108

TINA: I know it hurts. *(Pause)* They're in charge of everything. Everything. They influence what you eat. They influence what you wear. They tell you how much you earn. They take what they want. Then they make bombs. 'For your own good' they say. Play mind-tricks. Make me buy things I don't want. Influence everything! Even tell you how to make love right!

KOLA: Just shut up Tina, you're not helping me.

TINA: All right, so the man gave you a soul-strapping. What else is new?

KOLA: He's a man! He's got balls, and so have I!

TINA: He's paying your salary. He pays your rent. Puts food in your belly. *(Kola pretends he doesn't hear)*.

KOLA: There's an evil there. A malignant Evil. But I can't touch it. It's there but I can't touch it.

TINA: There's evil everywhere. It's man's inheritance. It comes from having beasts as ancestors.

KOLA: Back home in Africa, where ordinary men are deified, it's very difficult to claim a common ancestory with a baboon! *(Pause)* There's an Evil here....an intelligent Evil. Deliberate. Conniving. Destructive. It lures men with such luscious baits and uses those very baits to destroy them!

TINA: Nonsense! Man is an intelligent being. He decides for himself what he wants and goes out to get them, no matter the cost. He has a choice of using fair means.....or foul means.....

KOLA: No, this Evil is much too clever. Its bait isn't just in the the means by which man gets what he wants.....the real trap is in why he wants it. *(Thoughtfully)* Why he wants it...*(Getting suddenly excited)*....Tina, can't you see? Why did I come to London? To search for opportunities to become famous; to be discovered! To climb to the top of the celebrity list! To create a standard peasants would cherish and envy! To be worshipped! That's the culmination of my dream!

TINA: To be rich and powerful! For your boss to wonder if you're going to paint a macabre picture of him with biting words of power and bitterness!

KOLA: Yes! Yes! To make him go on his knees and beg for

forgiveness! Yes! To make him take back every word! 'You're under my employ. Your wages are £2.50 per hour. If found to be with a criminal record, I will fire you without notice. Understood?' I had no reply. I had to. I couldn't say 'stuff your job!' I couldn't. I couldn't tell him that where I come from, I am a prince. I am royalty. Not the way I was dressed. Not with me applying for a £2.50 an hour job.

TINA: You'll make him eat up all those words.....

KOLA: Every single one...

TINA: Because they hurt, each word hurts, Like a red-hot spike with 'slave' etched all over it, burning your soul!

KOLA: Yes!

TINA: To be rich and powerful! That's what you want! That's your dream! Reach out and take it! Take it!

KOLA: Yes!

TINA: Power! Influence! Fame! Reach out! Take it! Take it!

KOLA: Yes! Yes!

TINA: No matter the cost. It's yours! You deserve it. You're good. You know it. Make the world know it! No matter the cost! Don't count the cost!

KOLA: NO!!! *(Long Pause)*. The 'cost'. I cannot ignore the cost. That is the ultimate price. That is the ultimate bait of the intelligent evil. I cannot ignore the cost.

TINA: Then you will remain a dreamer, waiting for the 'one-off's'. The only competition you ever won in your life had to be shared, even if it was first prize. Even if your work is good, you have a flaw. You're a dreamer. The world has no time for dreamers. It locks them away. Appoints 'head-doctors' to tuck them out of sight. Ignoring the cost. That's the essential difference between those that make it, and those that don't.

(Kola looks like he's been dealt a crushing blow. Tina breathes heavily like one who's been in an exhaustive fight. The two refuse to look at each other. Slowly, Kola climbs up into his sanctuary, and starts to type).

110

KOLA: Dear John,

It hurts. She hurt me. She won this round. It seems now our relationship has entered a new dimension. Now the cruelty on the outside has crept in. I am planning my revenge. I want her to weep till her eyes fall out. She hurt me. There is an evil out there. It has crept into bed with us. Instead of caring, she scratches...corn-rows of blood mark the aftermath of our passion. I become aware of a desire to hurt her so deeply she can't touch it. We do not love each other. I think I know that now. But there is something that keeps us together. Hate? Curiosity? Lust? Masochism? Fear? I must go. I must plan my revenge.

Burning, K.

(Sophia and John in next situation. Sophia is obviously angry. John just ignores her. Gradually, her anger starts to boil over).

SOPHIA: Is that all you're going to say about it?

JOHN: We've gone over this a hundred times before. I am not interested.

SOPHIA: You are famous now John. You're a writer. You're known. You will practise what you preach!

JOHN: Are you mad? *(almost hitting her)*

SOPHIA: *(Taunting him)* Where is your manhood gone John? Lesser men would play wild congas on a woman who questions their masculinity!

JOHN: *(Making an attempt to control his anger)* My fight is not with you...

SOPHIA: Then who? Who is the enemy John? Would he be conquered with paper and ink?

JOHN: All wars are not fought with muscle alone! We mustn't be accused of being all muscle and no brain!`

SOPHIA: We mustn't use that as an excuse to hide behind closed doors!

JOHN: What I am doing is important to the cause. I am a writer. The pen is mightier that the sword!

SOPHIA: *(With scorn)* Dreamer.

JOHN: *(Dangerously)* Don't bite off more than you can chew, woman!

SOPHIA: I can chew. I've got teeth, and I use them, to devour tough meat and to crush bones! Look out here John. Children are dying. Together, with them by my side, we face the harsh 'Kra ka ka, Kra ka ka' of automatic rifles, with sticks, stones and songs! *(Sadly)* You hide in here, doing you 'Kra ka ka' on a typewriter.

JOHN: I am a writer!

SOPHIA: Yes, I remember. 1st Prize. Joint winner. *(Mimics)* I am an angry voice that bellows with the fury of bloodthirsty Zulu warriors.....the only bloodthirsty Zulu warrior is the one that hides behind your pants! *(Starts to leave, then turns back)* You will speak John. The young ones want to hear you. If you refuse, I become the man. Mine will be the angry voice of our Zulu ancestors. You can sit at home and pound the mortar.

JOHN: *(Crushed he starts to compose, almost instinctively to counter the bitter truth)* "Dance children, dance! Dance young ones, dance! The poet dictates the tune. The stately boabab tree dances to the tune of the wind; the waves dance to the tune of the earth's pull; my soul dances to the tune of the enemy's death throes! Amandla! South Africa! You need my pen! You need my pen! Apartheid will dance to the tune of my pen! Mortar! Pounding! Pestle! Smashing! Apartheid! Dancing to the insistent pounding of my pestle! Shouting, Amandla! Freedom!" I am a Zulu warrior! My pen is my justifier. My instrument of Justice! Sophia! I am a man! I speak in a loud voice. Let the young ones read! Let them read! I must continue to pound!

SITUATION

Tina is sketching. Kola comes in from the outside. Tina ignores him. He flings his things on a chair and comes to peer over her shoulder. There's a silence as they both ignore each other. After a while Tina gets up, and chooses another brush, then settles down again.

KOLA: Hi!

TINA: *(Looking up at him as if she's just seen him)* Oh hi Kola! *(Reaches up and kisses him, almost too happily, then just as suddenly, her brightness disappears)* Why do we play these games Kola?

112

KOLA: Oh, I'm just imitating the natives. People here enjoy ignoring each other.

TINA: Racism is not your thing Kola. Don't get boring.

KOLA: Are you deaf or something? I said I'm just imitating the natives. I didn't say primitives! *(Long silence)* How are you?

TINA: *(Stunned, Tina stops painting)* What did you say?

KOLA: I said 'how are you?' And what are you acting so surprised for?

TINA: *(Pause)* I'm fine. And you?

KOLA: Don't get polite! Why are you people so polite?

TINA: *(Warningly)* Race Relations Board. They've got ears everywhere.

KOLA: I thought they were for our protection! You've got laws for everything that has the potential to embarrass. We're living in a quagmire of laws. Fear has taken up permanent residence on our backs! *(Another long pause)* You're becoming obsessed with children all of a sudden. Why is she clutching a bodyless arm?

TINA: It's an experiment. I'm digging into her unconsciousness....

KOLA: Whose unconsciousness?

TINA: *(Almost sharply)* The child's. Do you really want to know or are you just being polite?

KOLA: I really want to know. I'm sorry.

TINA: She is lonely. In a world where there don't seem to be any defined roles. She's angry. In a world where two people conceive her but have no idea who she is; what she is; who she wants to be; and what she'll become....

KOLA: But...horn-rimmed glasses? A man's tie on a little girl's blouse?

TINA: Those are her father's.

KOLA: *(Starting to get agitated)* The make-up? The expensive jewellery? The high heels.

TINA: Those are her mother's.

KOLA: She's sucking her thumb.

TINA: She's five years old.

KOLA: Then why's smoke coming out of her mouth?

TINA: That's the experiment. The picture is an allegory.

KOLA: I don't get it.

TINA: *(Light-hearted, almost dreamy)* She's conceived and born. Her environment is hostile. She knows. She knows she's not wanted. She felt it everytime the bottle was rammed into her mouth; everytime her pushchair jostled and vibrated. She felt the hostility. The resentment. The dislike.

KOLA: What are you saying?

TINA: The horn-rimmed glasses? She became her own father. The jewellery...

KOLA: *(Disbelief)* She became her own mother?

TINA: And the smoke? The fumes of the drugs that provided sporadic bliss...

KOLA: Nobody'll buy it!

TINA: And finally, the high heels. Her make-up. Disguises. To satisfy the consciences of her middle-aged lovers, who pretended not to see the pain..

KOLA: Why do you do it

TINA: *(As if suddenly coming to her senses)* Do what?

KOLA: Distort everything you sketch?

TINA: You do it all the time!

KOLA: But you're not me! What sort of mind would create such a rape of innocence?

TINA: You tell me.

KOLA: I don't like this Tina! Who in their right senses would exhibit monstrosities? You've got your future to think of Tina. You're good, but people'll think that you're mad!

TINA: Did people think Picasso was mad? This is what I see. Can't you understand? This is what I see! Tell me Kola, what do you see when you walk out in the streets? What do you see? Or have you caught the disease too? Avoiding the eyes of young people, just in case you see the pain? Why talk about an airy-fairy evil, when you're too scared of what people will say about you? You're scared!

KOLA: I'm not scared!

TINA: What about the volumes of poetry in there? Who's going to appreciate them? You?

KOLA: But I...

114

TINA: Won a joint-prize for poetry. Then what? What Kola? Did you come to London to kiss arse, or to represent a rich and thriving culture? You want the applause of these people so bad you can smell it. It stinks! Of desperation. Of fear. Of unrealized frustrated dreams....

KOLA: *(Angry)* The young ones. I see their pain; in their aggression. Their...frustration; in their anger. Their cry for help; in their drugs. But what can I do about it? At home, I am a prince. A real prince. When my father dies, I become the king of a big and proud town. I am a proud man. But how erect can a man stand, when people are faced with his nakedness? That is why in my language, we have a saying, that "the wise man lies prostrate in greeting, while his insides stand erect!" If I climb to the top here, I bring glory to my country and to my Kingdom...

TINA: It's not worth it.

KOLA: I have a mission!

TINA: Stop lying to yourself!

KOLA: You are talking to a prince! "Omode o mogun, on pe lefo"! You're a child who mistakes potent charms for vegetables!

TINA: Go out and prove it. Prove you're not scared of them. Of their carefully worded criticism! Prove it! Prove you're not scared of their scorn. If you're that good, go out and prove it!

(Silence. Long silence. Kola seeks escape)

KOLA: Does she think of suicide? This creature you've given life. Does she desire to fling that gift right back in your face? *(Tina does not reply)* I need to know if she'd rather die than live this life you've created for her! *(Still she doesn't reply)* Would she rather die than live a life which holds nothing for her? No future, just an ever present past? *(Grabs his head and moans)*

TINA: *(Flatly, after pause)* She's dead.

KOLA: Oh God, no....

TINA: We used to be kids together. *(Kola is wracked with sobs, but tears don't flow. Transforming gradually, Tina melts with compassion, and starts to comfort him)* It doesn't matter. You don't have to prove anything to anybody. You're human. You're sensitive. And you're beautiful...

KOLA: If only there's someone I can hold responsible for this....anger

115

that threatens to consume me....someone who can take the brunt of this mad fury ....but there's nobody there.....I cannot identify any faces....just a mass; a mad, pulsating mass of flesh that doesn't care.....as long as it's satisfied. A selfish, mindless, cruel...*(struggling with the abuse as if verbally hitting people, so that Tina flinches at the venom)*....stupid, opinionated...no, it's not you I'm angry with...*(Tina kneels next to him)*...don't kneel to me...please don't kneel....*(She rests his head on her breasts, and soothes him like a child)* It's not you I'm angry with....you know that don't you?

TINA: I know. Now, we go to bed...

KOLA: I don't want to make love.

TINA: *(Nodding)* Me neither.

KOLA: We hurt each other too much.

TINA: Yes.

KOLA: And afterwards, we hate each other some more....until the sweat dries..

TINA: *(Slight Pause)* Yes.

KOLA: No love. No compassion. No tenderness. Like animals.

TINA: Yes. *(Pause)* Tonight, we just hold each other. Tomorrow, write John. Work on your masterpiece. Anger fuels your writing. Tonight, we just forget the world. Even ourselves. Tonight, we just hold each other.

(Still cradling his head, she holds him tightly his arms curl round her)
FADE.

Dear John,

This, for me is admitting defeat. I am unfamiliar with the word. But we've lost something precious, something sacred in our relationship. This will be for me, a means of holding unto that sacredness, no matter what. This will be different from the usual letters you receive. Why? Because these are letters you will not receive. How do I start? Where do I start? Writing letters is not like wading through a fog of tear-gas. It is harder for me. It is harder still because I must face the reality of perhaps dying before I get the chance to say 'I love you'.

Now I find that I look at you often; as if, etching your features so

116

completely in my spirit. I had no right to say those words to you. But I was angry. The anger remains, but it's I it consumes. Today, I discovered something funny. You and I, we know very little of each other. Even after three years. Three years of University together. Three years of intimacy. But do you know who I am? Do I know who you are? It didn't really matter then, but suddenly, it matters now.
Sophia.

Dear Kola,
Your past few letters have betrayed a mind bent on a futile search, a search that leads only to hurt and despair. Why must you ask so many questions? Sometimes, it's like you hold someone, or something responsible for the way the world is; the way your country is; the way South Africa is.

Your thought-provoking ideas are idealistic. There they remain; in the domain of long forgotten dreams; ear-marked by the cob-webbed, forgotten graves of those who dreamed them. We live in a society, Black, yellow, green, or white, where people live only for the joy of subjecting others to the soles of their oppressive and expensive feet; a society where no other rules seem to work except that of violence and destruction. In such a situation, you don't ask questions. You find out in which category you fall, and obey the rules. You fight the same enemy, hate the same things, eat the same food, make love to the same woman. Perhaps you think my definition of solidarity is too extreme. But what do you know Kola? How can you know?

It's tiring to talk about the dominion of the white-man. A popular phrase: 'White-man'. A symbol that generations of Black writers have used as a source of their venomous inspiration! Baring the fangs of Africa's unquenchable anger when roused! Flexing the muscles of the python, which squeezes greed out with man's mysterious breath of life; leaving surplus carrion for the old and bald vultures, who feast happily, unquestioning, indifferent to the circumstances that have provided a sumptious feast for those who feed on dead meat.

We are justified to use violence to reclaim that which is ours. An oppressor is a bully. A bully uses strength to frighten a small one. But

117

once the small one bites deep and hard into corrupt flesh....fear makes a nesting place in the bosom of the bully. Duck, small one, duck! Duck below the flailing fists of the desperate one. Draw blood. Suck deeply, then spit out the poison for all to see! Sophia represents the fury and courage of our women, who fight on despite the blood that drips from their wombs. You run from the realities of Africa, and worry about the morality of England.
Worried John.

Dear John,
Are you disappointed in me? Why? You mention reality and morality. You accuse me. Why? You call me a dreamer. Is it wrong to dream dreams? Or is it wrong to explore them? Can you separate morality from reality? Is it possible to maintain reality without a universal definition of what is wrong and what is right? And by what yardstick do we measure right or wrong? Who enforces this moral law? A Super-power? Britain? The United States? Russia? The 'United States' of Africa? Who, John? And if we do not have such a governing body, how do we define morality? How do we define reality?
We do not have the answers John, the world doesn't have the answers. That scares me. And what I see here, scares me. For I see lost people. I see, desperation and despair....and defeat. That scares me John. I came here looking for answers. <u>Sure</u> that I'd find the answers. It's not just the violence John, it's everything. Everything! I feel cheated. Lied to. The West gave the impression they had the answers. We have different functions. You fight the <u>effects!</u> I must find the <u>causes.</u>
Kola.

My Beloved,
Oh how my heart aches with the love that wells up deep within my breast! It beats a rhythm of its own; erratic; depthless. The blood that flows in the channels of my veins responds to its call. The high tides of raw passion combine with soft gentle winds to play such music that calms this restless urge in my spirit.
Beloved! The songs we offered on the altar of the life we defined,

echo deep within me...and there I dwell, unwilling to let go of the heaven we discovered; a heaven without staple mealies; without deceit; without betrayals and treachery, without broken and strewn lives; without fear dancing the Samba in our hearts, like a suddenly decapitated chicken, its blood crying out for revenge as it begins its ritualized journey from boiling water into variously sized stomachs!

I just sit and cry sometimes, John. How can I make you know just how real this love is? How can I make you see, when all you want is the applause of the world at your cleverness at manipulating words? How would you take the news that we danced the dance of our elders, and now we have aching feet to prove it? I speak in parables even to myself. You need the kernel of wisdom to crack this one.
Sophia.

(John comes rushing down from his 'santuary'. He is genuinely angry. Sophia is writing as well, dressed in what look like combat fatigues, but subtly so).

JOHN: *(Waving a piece of paper in her face)* Listen to this! 'But I've been thinking John, who are we to appoint ourselves the conscience of society?' Sometimes, this Kola is a fool! We are the conscience of society! Things other people shrug off make us cringe with embarrassment! Injustice makes us cringe! Murder makes us cringe! Pain and suffering resurrect the brute in us!
SOPHIA: Why are you angry with him?
JOHN: I am not angry! We have a divine vocation...
SOPHIA: You have not answered his question. Who are you to appoint yourselves the consciences of society?
JOHN: You don't understand...
SOPHIA: Perhaps you're right. Perhaps I don't. And perhaps you're angry with him because he is asking questions you wouldn't dare ask yourself....
JOHN: Listen. Writing is a gift. From where, I don't know. But I know this. It has power! The power of a pestle crushing corngrains in a stoic mortar!

119

SOPHIA: What else did he say!

JOHN: *(Relunctantly has to stop trying to justify himself)* Does society have a conscience? Can it have a conscience? A collective conscience? That seems to me wholly impossible; for such a conscience would be a complex composite of good and evil; fair and foul; honest and dishonest; judge and prosecuted; oppressed and oppressor. Artists are not exempt from the curious duality that exists in mankind. To expose, we must be equally prepared to be exposed. *(There is a silence that neither is quite prepared to break, but Sophia is aware of John's struggle inside)*

SOPHIA: Are you afraid of Kola, John?

JOHN: What sort of question is that?

SOPHIA: When you speak of him now, I sense something...dislike?

JOHN: Nonsense.

SOPHIA: Envy? *(John doesn't reply)* What is it, John? Why are you afraid of him asking questions?

JOHN: I'm not afraid of him asking questions!

SOPHIA: Then try to answer them. That way, you'll grow. I'll grow. Then we can meet the challenges of our society.

JOHN: He doesn't know all the answers!

SOPHIA: But he doesn't pretend to! That's why he's asking you. He's searching. He respects you, respects your opinion. For a man who's never met you, he confides in you, John, he's like your brother....

JOHN: He's writing an African Epic....

SOPHIA: Meet his challenge John....meet his challenge.....

FADE TO KOLA AND TINA

(Kola is seated, curled up with Tina in his arms. They are listening to the sound of children playing and laughing. It's like music. They sit, entranced by the beautiful sound)

KOLA: It's like music. The sound of a child's laughter is like music.

TINA: Like...music.

KOLA: No thoughts, no worries....just laughter, sunshine and toys.

TINA: Sunshine and toys....*(Then she starts to cry)* ...it hurts....it hurts..

KOLA: Not all of them laugh...some have bruises...some are punch bags some grow up so fast...not missing the sunshine...not minding the pain....

120

TINA: Then...they pass it on...this disease...of hurt, unhappiness of guilt...of deep, knotted pain...of a bleak existence....an emotional trap...then they strike out...in frustration...in despair...in resignation...*(Looking at Kola)* When will you tell me...

KOLA: Tell you what?

TINA: That you love me...tell me you love me....with your heart, not your mouth...with your soul....sober, not when we're locked in our sweaty embraces, not when passion unlocks our tongues and we promise each other the world.....no, no,...sober....when we are accountable for the things we say, and the responsibility we accept....tell me now, Kola, please, t..te..tell me now, now, tell me you love me, and mean it!

KOLA: *(Struggling all this time inside)* I can't. *(Tina instantly turns cold)* I just can't. I don't know what love is. And neither do you. (Walks towards his 'santuary')

TINA: Yes. Write John. Tell him about the laughter of the children. Ask if they still have any down there. Children must be extinct in South Africa.

KOLA: Dear John,

The greatest tragedy on earth, is that I must grow into adulthood and lose the innocence of youth. Loss of youthful ideals which I nurtured in university, and an assimilation into the system is as sure as I am a man, and I have genitals to prove it.

I look into the skies, on pathetic sunny days, and angrily address whatever force is out there. I ask him/her/it: Why have you created this farce? When did you lose control? Why did you lose control? But there's no reply. This paradox of existence baffles me. For what purpose is there so much pain, and suffering and absolute evil?

And yet, for what purpose are there tears of relief, joy, happiness and love? Why is there such a kaleidoscope of both evil and good? Why in such terrible conditions are we able to recognise courage, dignity and character? What is the miracle of holding a woman in your arms, no, not sex, just the utter intimacy that's a result of knowing you choose not to take advantage of the accessibility of a brief moment of passion?

Tina cried today John. It's a miracle 'cos...I cried too. It felt good. It felt real. I didn't feel any less a man. I was able to face myself with the

121

fact that tears coursed down my face, and mingled with Tina's. Tina and I have not made love in over a month. There doesn't seem to be a need to. We lie in bed and just hold each other. Sometimes, I read poetry to her:

"Oh to be but a child again,
Remembering no pain,
Remembering only the breast on
Which this head has lain
Remembering the strong furrowed
backs, strengthened by the pride
And joy of fertility,
The backs on which this one rode
Dreaming dreams of wild
Antelopes, of delicious
Bush-rats...
Remembering, oh remembering, the stinging
Yet soothing palms, on naked buttocks
The discipline
The palm that brushed away the tears.
To be but a child again.
Remembering no pain.
Remembering only the breast
On which
this head has lain."

But she really wants to hear me say that I love her. But I can't.
Not until I find out what love means. She's still hurting.
But for now, she's satisfied.

How long will this calm before the storm last? I don't know. Today, I heard music...children laughing....playing....singing.
Lovely....Soothing...Tina asks if there are still children out there.....or do they throw stones with their nappies still wet?
Disoriented. Kola.

122

(Sophia has been reading this letter. John finds her doing so but doesn't complain. He leaves sanctuary, and out. Sophia follows him. Silence. Freeze John)

Oh John my love!
You do not understand, do you? Have you forgotten so soon our performances of your poetry? Alone? Far away from prying eyes? Our celebration of life even as vacuums were created. Friends. Family. Foe. Our celebrations of love, of hope, of peace! Have you forgotten, John? We two were one, hurting together, sharing together, loving together....what happened?
I was searching for our intimacy, John. That search revealed another world within which you say I have no place. It hurts John. I cannot tell you how much. Perhaps if I didn't love you so much ...perhaps if I didn't carry such virile proof of that love....perhaps if South Africa didn't have Apartheid...I could go on and on John. I was searching for our intimacy. Forgive me. Sophia.

SITUATION
(Light on the two. Stage in darkness)

TINA: Kola...
KOLA: Hmmm?
TINA: Who are you?
KOLA: Sometimes, I wonder. Sometimes, I don't want to know.
TINA: You're like what a ghost would be. Sometimes, I see you, sometimes I can't. But either way, I can't seem to hold you.
KOLA: Coming here was like trying to define the roots of a people whose culture and way of life are so intertwined with mine, that it's almost impossible to separate them.
TINA: And now?
KOLA: Look at me. I'm wearing traditional attire. This is called a buba, and this is a sokoto, and this, a fila. This watch is made in Britain. My underwear bears a tag made in Britain. Even the complexities of the words I manipulate belong here. It doesn't matter where the clothes I wear come from. That's not the issue. The issue is the amount of

123

influence the West has over Africa.

TINA: So you came here...

KOLA: Yes...

TINA: To find your second roots?

KOLA: To define my major one, which has become obscured by the second one...

TINA: Are you....disappointed?

KOLA: No. Just homesick. I miss the celebrations, the laughter. Even your enemies laughed you into your grave. The West has become trapped by its own definition of civilization. It asphyxiates itself everyday with laws created as a reaction, not as an action, independent, created without pressure. It is civilised not to laugh too hard; not to show emotion; to reduce everything to the practical realities of reason. Even then, your civilization and your politics don't concern me. This undefined subtle evil does.

TINA: Evil....

KOLA: Indifference. Indifference feeds it. It thrives on indifference.

SOPHIA: What do you want John?

JOHN: Can't a man expect any privacy around here anymore?

SOPHIA: What privacy can you expect from someone with whom you've shared your bed? Hmm? What is it that you hide that you have not already confessed to me while I held you in my arms?

JOHN: Leave me alone Sophia.

SOPHIA: Perhaps that is best. *(Thoughtfully)*

JOHN: You know I didn't mean that.

SOPHIA: Perhaps. But who knows what you mean these days? Hmm? What is the point of this relationship John? When every time we are together, we each enter into different worlds to suffer alone. Hmm? What's the point? It's only when we make love that you share your heart with me. Why John? And the next day, we pretend you didn't say the things you said. And you resent me some more, because I was there, and I heard.

JOHN: Stop this foolishness!

SOPHIA: I mean it John. Perhaps it's time I left you alone. Perhaps I'm interrupting your destiny.

JOHN: What do you want me to say woman? That I love you?

TINA: *(Breaking the mood)* Is there evil in this room, Kola?

KOLA: Sometimes.

TINA: Is it in my work?

KOLA: Sometimes. *(Light fades everywhere else except on a large canvas. Tina unveils it dramatically)*

TINA: Then this is evil.

SOPHIA: It's not what you say that matters John...

JOHN: *(Passionately)* I love you!

SOPHIA: *(Sadly)* It is not how you say it....

JOHN: *(Getting angry)* Then what is it?

SOPHIA: Respect. I need to respect you John. Too many women blind themselves to that. Money. Fame. Beauty. That doesn't impress me anymore John. I see death written on people's faces everyday. I have no further use for those things that impress other women. What is the use of money, if I can't live to spend it? What is the use of fame if I can't live to get drunk on it? What is beauty to me when tomorrow I can bear on my body the disfiguring scars of apartheid? No John. It's not just making love either. We can't make love all day. We can't stay locked together. Even if we wanted to. No. *(Pause)* What then do I want? I will tell you. Because I live everyday with the reality of my death, I want a man who is not afraid to face the reality of his.

JOHN: *(Coldly)* Are you calling me a coward?

SOPHIA: And who is a coward John? Do you know? Do I know? *(Starts to laugh)* Facing those monsters with sticks and stones, do you know how many times I wet my pants? *(Laughs some more)* Is that cowardice? Running defiantly into the nostrils of death, with driblets of fear-induced urine, hot and burning, sneaking down the insides of my thighs, forming pools in my shoes? At first, I felt shame. Then triumph! Because I was still running....in the direction of the enemy.....into the nostrils of death.

JOHN: I do not understand you.

SOPHIA: Is it not you who once wrote that there's poetry in death, and pain and tears? The poetry is out there, but you're writing in here, behind four walls, where you cannot see, where you cannot feel...

125

JOHN: You don't know what you're saying! How can I write if I don't feel?

SOPHIA: What do you feel John? Fear? Hot urine running down your thighs? A strange awareness of God? Of wondering why He's not doing anything? What do you feel John? How do you communicate a feeling you have never experienced? How?

KOLA: What is this?

TINA: Another allegory. Tears of blood. Pain. Indescribable agony. A prostitute who draws men into pits of perversion. A congregation of stupid men, who sacrifice everything for her. Then she makes them cry....shedding tears of blood....

KOLA: Destroy it!

TINA: There's more! You must listen! There's more!

KOLA: Destroy it!

TINA: The man with the lost look....the martyr....trying to make them see... trying to save them.....and his suitcase spilling endless letters....ghosts from a past that stain a present....

KOLA: Destroy it!

JOHN: *(Abruptly)* Who is he? *(Sophia's silent)* Who wants to take you away from me?

SOPHIA: Does it matter?

JOHN: I have a right to know!

SOPHIA: No-one.

JOHN: You're a liar!

SOPHIA: Don't ever say that to me John, ever!

JOHN: Who is he? Who is he?

SOPHIA: What would you do about it? Fight for me? There's no-one else John. The only one you have to fight is yourself! *(Sophia makes for the door. John runs and blocks her.)*

JOHN: No-one else will nest where I have sown! *(Starts to strangle her)* I have loved you! Now, I will share your pain!

TINA: A rainbow embraces a surly sky, its only colours, blood-red and black. A dark promise. A promise to give back, with generous interest as much pain and agony as is sufficient, to drive the world mad....

KOLA: There's only one promise, and it's a promise of hope, of an awakening! This is evil! Destroy it!

TINA: The fishbowl of water; only it's not water. That is her inspiration. It contains the salty tears of loneliness, which keeps emptying and refilling. On her face; those aren't tribal marks.....they are the irrigation ditches her eyes have dug in a futile hope of melting her hard and knotted heart...

KOLA: Destroy this obscenity!

TINA: It is art!

KOLA: It is evil!

TINA: You set off searching for this evil. Now I've located it for you. Destroy it yourself!

SOPHIA: John let go!

(He chokes her the more. Suddenly, she knees him in the groin. Screaming and clutching his genitals, he drops on the floor, with a look of total horror on his face. Massaging her neck, she stands looking at him, then resolutely, while he groans and moans, she turns and starts to walk away)

JOHN: Don't....don't leave me....*(she stops)*....Don't leave me Sophia....forgive me...l love you.....don't leave....

SOPHIA: Perhaps I am interrupting your destiny John. God would never forgive me if I did.

JOHN: Don't leave me like this....please....

SOPHIA: Don't make this unbearable for me. I must respect you. You must respect yourself. You can't say you love me, then hurt me in such a way that only you can. I can't stand the hurting anymore. If I stay, one day, you'll kill me. And I don't want to die! I want to love a man, not a dreamer....a man! A man I can trust my children with if I die....A man I know will soothe the pain away....I can't mother you any more John! I'm tired. I want to rest too. But there's no strength there. I'm tired. I can't mother you any more. *(She leaves)*

JOHN: Mother of my life! Don't go! Fount of my inspiration! Don't desert me nowwwwww!! *FADE*

KOLA: *(Kola is afraid of it. He recoils at Tina's suggestion)* Destroy it!

TINA: You love me don't you Kola? I know you do.....I just want to hear you say...Tina, I love you....

KOLA: Destroy it! *(Attacks the canvas and viciously destroys it)*

TINA: You must save me....from running....from running so hard after ghosts....after illusions....I'm tired Kola.....I'm tired of all this fighting. What are we trying to prove? I just want someone to love me, that's all....I'm tired of having to prove myself to people. I just want to be me. *(Kola walks to her and holds her in his arms)*

KOLA: She draws me....
Even as fertile pollen attracts busy bees.
Even as coy sands draw
the amorous attention
Of insistent waves.
Trailing brittle twig on
silent....crystalline...beaches
Our spirits search; soaring like
watchful eagles;
Searching the impossible, infinite
Expanse of this mystery;
Of footprints in sodden sand
A work of art, delicate and intricate,
Too lost in this mystery which engulfs us
To notice the sad destruction of art uncherished
Unnoticed, Unappreciated.
And yet, she draws me...
from vain apparels of finite knowledge...
Stumbling over
simple
truths
Caught in the trap of established foolishness
Entangled in a web of presumptuous preconceptions
Smothered in a growing awareness of my
erected
elevated

exalted
empirical
errors
embarrassment at my
fecund
fallacies; at my
fabricated falsehoods.
Here we are. The trail abandoned;
Brittle twig broken
In three places.
Before a humbling sky, with the sea,
and the wind
and the birds
and distant humanity
forming the orchestra that witness this moment of
truth
composing a score that humbles Mankind....
I will allow these searching spirits rest.
Tina, I love you. *(Embraces her. Snarling without warning)*
TINA: Liar! *(She breaks free. Kola catches her and kisses her. She breaks free again and slaps him)* Bastard!
KOLA: *(Stunned)* Tina? *(She stops, heaving. Kola moves to her and they embrace)*
TINA: I'm sorry. *FADE*

Dear John

I have written a room-full of letters since I left you. I know that you think there's someone else. I know that you will concentrate on hating me. Perhaps I shut myself away from the reality of that happening, by always remembering those beautiful times when you would hold me in your arms and compose poetry inspired by the love you and I share.

It feels like death John, this separation from you. Like death. I don't like death. I cannot live in this limbo. And yet, it seems we burnt our bridges that night. You see John, I was quite willing to die by your hands. I was willing to stare in your eyes and proclaim my love even as you choked breath out of me. But I couldn't. Not because I'm afraid to die. But because I'm a fighter. I fight for what is mine, by right. My life was not yours to take away. It was mine to give. You did not ask for me to give it. I'd be dead and moulding in the grave now John, with the hundreds of thousands that have gone before, if you'd asked for my life. It would have been the only true way to show you how I truly love you.

Your friend is right to ask questions. But there's nobody there qualified to answer them. Only God can. And He's not talking. John, South Africa needs more people like you; who care, and are sensitive; but also, it needs more people like me, who would fight boldly with urine-stained trousers.

I am afraid John. Afraid of this aloneness. Afraid of this emptiness. It seems like despair. And our country is being raped. Our people feel this helplessness when they squat in shanty-town...in the homelands. Where are we going now? I am afraid. Mandela's greying. Biko's gone. Themba's gone. Luthuli's gone. How many more must go John? I am afraid.
Sophia.

(Kola and Tina are in the middle of a fight. Tina exposes his fears and attacks them. Kola retaliates with violence.)

KOLA: I'm warning you

TINA: Show me this proud African prince who's supposed to be the hero of his people...

KOLA: Leave my heritage out of this Tina! You don't understand heritage and you don't understand culture!

TINA: Oh, but I understand dignity, and pride, in myself; in reality, not in some stupid, deluded dream!

KOLA: Are you tired of life, you miserable woman? Are you tired of life?

TINA: You touch me, and they'll string you up without even the benefit of a trial!

KOLA: Do you think I care? What makes you think I care if your laws stifle my freedom? I'm just warning you, if I catch you in there again, where you don't belong....

TINA: *(Interjecting)* Amongst your impotent rantings against society? In the pathetic little paradise you've created; in the world of make-believe where everybody is nice and considerate; where people don't even notice you've got dark skin? A world where you're not cleverly reminded that your ancestors once bowed, scraped and grovelled and delighted in the privilege of calling the white man 'sir'?

KOLA: *(Lets loose a burst of abuse, then starts to sing)* Ko ni daa fun e! Iwo kini kan jati jati yii!

Asin to oun to akere....joo mi jo,

Awon loo jo on ja....joo mi jo,

Ija ree mo wa la.....Chorus *(Pointing to her and dancing around her at the same time)* Laa sin ge mi nimu je....Chorus

Egba mi lowo re......Chorus

You stupid bitch! Who do you think I'm doing this for? Me? What would it take to get it into your stupid, ignorant head, the depth and the sophistication of the evil that is threatening to swallow us all, whole? You, like the little rat with sharp buck teeth in the song, have bitten my nose off, because I interfered in a fight that will destroy you! You haven't asked yourself the relevant question. Why am I concerned with your society? Because your society has left its peculiar influence on mine and that influence has mutated, and become a problem peculiar to my society and my people!

When I see the children here, I see a breed my society would have spawned in less than a quarter of a century. But in either case, the children have no choice! They are the victims of society. Inheritors to a past they want to forget. Initiators of a future that might not be there. And the present? There is no present. Because it's influenced by the dark cloud of the past, and it in turn influences a bleaker future! My only concern is for the children. Society has no right to condemn them to a future they had no part in making.

TINA: *(Laughingly)* What are you doing in there then? Why haven't you produced your work to the people who would reduce you to next to nothing, you dreamer? The critics with the power to make or break you? Dreamer! Bubbling with ideas, but without guts, or the stomach to face the flak! They won't love you for telling the truth! They'll make sure the world will never hear your voice again!

KOLA: No more. You will no longer herald the death of this dream *(Moves towards her)*

FADE LIGHTS ON 'SANTUARY' ONLY. EFX OF SLAPS AND BEATING FORMS THE BACKGROUND KOLA'S LETTER.

Dear John,

Help me. Help me. I am drowning. This evil must destroy me before I expose it, and destroy it. It's everywhere, even inside me. This anger, it scares me. I lose my head......I....I lose control.

Help me. Please. Help me....

JOHN: Dear Kola,

Perhaps all who create must feel as you feel. Because we are exposed to a realm that ordinary eyes do not perceive. Emotion becomes a whirlpool; a hurricane; a thunderstorm within which the pain people feel mingles with our own. How much pain can this body take? How much pain was it designed to take? Anger is a good emotion. It purifies......

KOLA: It burns! Its like an active volcano. Once it explodes you can't contain its fury!

JOHN: But my friend, isn't that when it's at its best? Hmm? Anger tamed or rationalized is anger castrated! Anger purifies...

KOLA: By what definition? Justified anger? Against my fellowman? Doesn't that give me the licence for murder? What differentiates me from two snarling dogs on the streets if I justify my anger? And if I don't, how do I rid myself of this tearing and bubbling acid in my soul???

JOHN: And what sort of anger do you unleash on a human being like you, who shares your pain, and suffers in a way unique to every individual? Whose only means of vengeance is to strike out at the one whose sweat becomes one with yours; one whose body, soul and spirit becomes one, with yours?

JOHN: You frighten me! When we do not have the answers, why must we ask the questions? When we hurt, and our souls feel bleak and empty, anger resuscitates us! Enflames us! Emboldens us! Why must you ask these questions?

KOLA: I hit Tina today. There is something frightening about hitting someone else. A release. Of tension. Then something else ...A heaviness...or more like...like .....a....tearing in my soul....a feeling of dread....of fear. I am familiar with the feeling. Like once when my mother caught me with my hand in her soup pot, with my indictment written in oil over my mouth, between my teeth, under my finger nails....everywhere. It was the feeling of guilt.

JOHN: And as you do everything else, you must explore the phenomenon of guilt. Why do you feel guilt? Because mama has taught that stealing is wrong. It is typed into the computer-bank of your unconsciousness, and reinforced with stinging strokes of the cane. You were taught guilt....

KOLA: Yes, I was punished, when I deserved it. Occasionally when I didn't, but this time, it was different. Y'see, my mother trusted me. And I...I betrayed that trust. My conscience confirmed that my punishment was deserved. But John, my punishment was nothing compared to what I went through inside. Guilt. Guilt John. When I hit Tina, I felt that guilt. I felt something else. And that really scares me. I wanted to go on hitting her, I lost control! I enjoyed it! I enjoyed my power over her! I enjoyed it!

JOHN: You scare me. Anger is a good emotion. If I·lose that, I lose steam. My work needs that steam. Like in every war, there are always casualties Always. Innocents suffer the most.

KOLA: John....

JOHN: She left me Kola. She's gone. Without the anger, I am nothing but a husk.

Your friend, John.

(Kola is on his knees for this scene. Tina is silhouetted and her voice is seemingly disembodied. It's both mocking, contemptuous and pitying at the same time.)

KOLA: The shrill protesting cries of the Black sacrificial cock combine with tolling bells, all pathetic attempts at reaching a silent Creator....

TINA: Tina Ross. Twenty-one. The little girl with the horn-rimmed glasses; the designer tie; the expensive obscene jewellery, and tottering on her mothers stilts.....

KOLA: Who is it that walks on my grave? Who is it that resurrects pain administered with the precision of a master surgeon? Who is that who listens to the silent echoes of a voiceless scream?

TINA: Tina Ross. Teenage doper. Sex-toy extra-ordinaire! To quote a favourite term, 'used and abused! 'Deprived of a future, devoid of a past; destroying the present by destroying the dreams that others dare to dream. Bitch and bastard, Tina Ross....

KOLA: Who is it that moans in the dead of night, stalking and prowling while the innocent sleep? Unhappy with joy; embittered by laughter, scornful of love?

TINA: Tina Ross. Teenage self-murderer. Queen of the night times; the aggressive leather-jackets; the 'statement' haircuts; intimidating poses and holsters with cans of graffiti spray. The little girl that died asking: "Why was I brought into this stupid world???"

(Lights isolate both Tina and Kola-pools of light. Tina's silhouette disappears, and now she's bathed in harsh lighting. This is a new Tina. A hard Tina. From this point on, Kola seems dazed and delirious.)

KOLA; Gloat vultures, gloat... Fragmented dreams! Insistent warning. Fragmented dreams! Fracturer of dreams. Fracturer of dreams! Each day you screamed... Fractured dreams!

TINA: Why should humanity be saved from the cry of desperation and the wrath of the unloved breed it spawns? What right do you have to search for the answers? Nobody wants to know the answers! I was the prostitute in the painting you destroyed. I wrecked homes, destroyed families. You were the poor deluded martyr, your hope-filled and questioning letters to South Africa your indictment. You cannot identify the evil. Thus, you cannot destroy it.

KOLA: *(In agony)* Fragmented dreams!

TINA: They'll never acknowledge, let alone applaud you, unless you're willing to ignore the cost. You've got a king-sized ego, Kola. You expect the world to play by your rules. That's why you're a dreamer. But a dreamer with such conviction and stupid naivete might just hit on the right combination. I couldn't allow that. I am sorry.

(With a wild bellow of anger and pain, Kola springs up and dashes for the silhouetted figure) BLACKOUT. The next scene is between John and Sophia. John is seen holding her heaving, torn and bloodied body. He is crying. Sophia's letters are strewn everywhere around them both.

JOHN: You cannot die! You cannot die!
SOPHIA: You were......not meant to....to read....the letters....
JOHN: Why didn't you tell me? Shake me! Bite me! Where is all the blood coming from? Where is everybody? Why did they leave you here like this? *(Lifts her to run out with her).*
SOPHIA: *(Pain in her voice)* Look, beloved, look between my thighs....is the blood coming....from....from....between....between my thighs? *(To which John lets out a guttural and tortured scream)* You must be strong, my love. Each life sacrificed so that our people may soar like eagles to freedom is a worthy sacrifice, one that must be celebrated, not mourned. Perhaps...perhaps if the child....perhaps....I am just sorry that both our causes became more important than each other....sorry that we didn't give our love full expression....love me all the same.....love me...

SLOW FADE AS JOHN STARTS TO CRY, HARSH SOBBING TEARS.

KOLA: *(Dull and lifeless)* Dear John,
What song do the children sing as they lie dying? Does it ease the pain, this song? Do they sing it clearly, sweetly and serenely, or do they choke on it, blood gurgling in their tortured throats?

And after the day's dose of tear-gas and pain, do the children hug each other? Or do they dance steps your people are so famous for? Do they know why their friends are fed to the ravenous monster called apartheid? Do they know?

Because the dawn is breaking; of a new beginning; of a mission accomplished; of a desire fulfilled; to choose; to make a choice right or wrong and to satisfy a craving for an undisputed identity. That identity is manifest in a choice freely made, for better or for worse. The children must know. They must understand. Otherwise, they'll question. Sooner or later. Otherwise they won't thank you for teaching them how to fight, but not how to offer the arm of peace.

Yours, K

(The final scene. Scene opens with typing sounds echoing ferociously. There's a sudden quiet knock on the door. The typing stops. The knock is heard again.)

KOLA: Go away! *(Starts to type again. Again the insistent and patient knock)* Are you deaf or something? Go away! *(Typing commences. Again the knock. Angrily, Kola tears out the pages and flings it on the floor)* Why don't you just take the door with you on your way out? Tear it off! *(From the darkness, a pregnant woman leans against the wall and stares at Kola)* What do you want? *(Silence)* Listen, I don't want what you've got to sell. So take your time, take a couple of deep breaths, then turn around and go away. Please.

WOMAN: I've just walked up about seventy steps.

KOLA: It's easier going down. Now what can I do for you?

WOMAN: I've got a message for you.

KOLA: Who from?

WOMAN: I heard your typing from the front door. Do you pay extra not to get thrown out?

KOLA: That's none of your business. What's the message? *(Ignoring him, she sees the crumpled letter in the light and picks it up)* Give that to me...

WOMAN: A time to question; a time to search; a time to hurt; a time to cry....*(Kola snatches the letter)*

KOLA: Go away! Go!

WOMAN: A time to hurt; a time to cry....; a time to face up to the reality of our situations. A time to crush skulls. A time to bury our dead. The Zulu warrior sends his greetings. They echo a bit, but don't worry. His breath sends shivers down my back, but don't take heed. The Zulu warrior sends greetings.

KOLA: What are you talking about?

WOMAN: John Mbiti shouts 'hail'! A raging salute to the blood-brother he has never seen.

KOLA: John? John Mbiti sent you? You're from South Africa? But how did you get here? Who are you? How is he?

WOMAN: Your letters flatter you. Empty words. From an empty skull. Words formed the backbone of your illusions. That's all they were; illusions.

KOLA: Did I say something wrong?

WOMAN: I am Sophia. John's woman.

KOLA: Sophia? But he said you...

WOMAN: Left him. I did. John is dead. *(The words strike Kola with a force that sends him reeling)* I should have left him alone. I shouldn't have desecrated the shrine upon which he communed with God without even knowing it.

KOLA: Sophia....

SOPHIA: Another notch for the statistics.

KOLA: I'm sorry I was rude. People come....undesirables. The guy upstairs sells heroin. They come knocking on my door. I've got to shout. It keeps them out. Please make yourself at home. You must eat, and rest. You've just walked up seventy steps....

SOPHIA: I won't be staying long. Not here anyway. It would be like breathing the same air with the woman who sneaks into my bed and steals the pleasure meant for me.

KOLA: But Sophia....

SOPHIA: Don't caress my name! I don't like you! For over a year I watched as you created a void between me and the man I loved. I read all your letters! Tried to find out what it was that fascinated him about you; tried to find out what was going on inside your head. But I couldn't. All I found was a large question mark. Who is Kola Bolarinwa? All John kept discussing was Kola. Kola. Kola. Kola.

137

Kola!! I had your name coming out of my ears. Kola. Kola. Kola!

KOLA: I am so sorry....

SOPHIA: Is your sorrow supposed to make everything better? My man is dead and you're alive and that makes me angry!

KOLA: And me? How do you think I feel?

SOPHIA: I don't care how you feel! John and I danced the dance of our elders, and I have his child as proof of our aching feet! I have the responsibility of explaining to it that its father died trying to prove that he was a man! That he lived trying to prove that he was more than a boil fated for a disinfected pin! That he lived trying to prove that he could be better than you.

KOLA: Sophia....

SOPHIA: Let me finish! You hounded him to death with your questions! You forced him to make a choice!

KOLA: We both spent the whole of our lives trying to run away from that one responsibility! We must make conscious choices!

SOPHIA: Was it also a conscious choice to beat up Tina while discussing the incompatibility of love and violence?

KOLA: Leave Tina out of this!

SOPHIA: Or the definition of your love for her? 'There are too many Tinas in London to worry about the fate of one'? Or does your definition of love include beating up the poor girl because she called you a dreamer?

KOLA: Maybe you're right. Maybe you had better go.

SOPHIA: When I'm ready. I've earned this hearing. And you will hear. You and John do not belong to this generation. Neither of you could stand violence. It was an evil. An evil that took over and seemed to manipulate you. You couldn't have that....

KOLA: Sophia, for the love of John, shut up!

SOPHIA: For the love of John, I must speak before you end up just like him; a feast for worms and millipedes! *(Long pause)* While you both sat behind your typewriters, I watched as my people started to ask each other; "What crime did we commit to attract this punishment"? I watched as voices grew hoarse, and some silent. I watched as some, burdened with it all, just lay down and waited for death. I watched as

John and I became strangers. And I hated you even more for making me compare you to him and question in my mind if Tina was the lucky one to have attracted the love of a man such as you. You made me doubt my love for John.

KOLA: Sophia...

SOPHIA: You are little more than a baby Kola. So was John. You explore an ideal you're not able to fulfil. You're human Kola. You cannot re-write the rules. *(Long pause)* Where's Tina?

KOLA: Tina is gone.

SOPHIA: Where?

KOLA: Gone. I don't know where.

SOPHIA: She's not coming back?

(Kola fetches a letter and gives it to her. She brings out a letter and gives it to him. Staring at each other, they bring out the contents. Sophia starts to read, but it's Tina's voice which echoes on stage)

My darling Kola,

I love you. I love you even more because you went on a journey to prove to me the depth of your love. It is too much for me. Everytime I hear children crying, it's the tears you shed for them that fills my sight. And when I hear them laugh, I see the child that lives within you, who will never grow old.

KOLA: I searched for love. I found it through her. I wanted to give my life for her. I wanted to marry her. But she couldn't handle it. She couldn't handle love....

SOPHIA: I'm going on a voyage of discovery too. I am looking for God. If you can love me that much, despite everything I did to humiliate you, then some sense might still emerge from the junkyard of my life, and the lives of people like me; the unwanteds and the unloveds. The frustrated and the desperates.

KOLA: She sought love desperately. Desperately. But she couldn't handle it. Men hurt her; took advantage of her; abused her; made her lose all sense of self-worth. That's what this is all about; People caring for each other.

SOPHIA: I know now that, some circumstances you cannot control, like

139

me coming into a world that didn't want me; but now, I know too that I can change those circumstances around and make my life what I want it to be.

KOLA: We had something special. It died when I told her I loved her. She's heard it so many times. The kind of love that dies after the last orgasm, and after the last drops of sweat have dried. The kind of love that inflicts pain; slaps and punches. Weals and bumps, aches and pain; and pain on the inside, deep, so deep you can't touch it; you can only gasp as the excruciating pain steals your screams and leaves you with inaudible groans....

SOPHIA: You located the evil, Kola. That's why you were afraid of my painting. The evil is in mankind. God must have the cure. So, I must search for Him. I must question Him. When I find Him, then, I must make a choice; whether to forgive Him and love Him, or to curse Him and reject Him. You're destined for greatness Kola. I am proud to have known you.

Love always, Tina.

KOLA: *(Reads John's letter, but it's John's voice we hear)*
   My friend,
This is a short letter. If you read this, it means I am dead. You forced me to come face to face with the fact that I hold my destiny in my hands, and I will not be remembered as one of those who didn't have the stomach to practise what they preached. I made private arrangements with Sophia long before she left me. You and Sophia, you are of the same spirit, take care of her..

   Once, I hated your guts. You made me work harder than I ever did in my life even in university. I envied you, even while solving problems you posed to me. Now I understand your plea for help when you hit Tina. I fully understand. This evil, it's inside us. Sometimes, it controls us. Don't quit. Ever. I love you. Remember me.
John Mbiti.

(Kola has tears in his eyes, and he's straining not to shed them.. Sophia moves to him and embraces him, tightly.)

SOPHIA: *(Choking back sobs)* It feels like coming back home...
KOLA: *(Whispering)* Yes....'ti ina ba ku, afi omo re ropo;
Bi adie ba ku, afi omo re ropo;
Bi igi ogede ba ku, afi omo re ropo;
Bi akinkanju enia ba ku, afi omo re ropo".

"When raging flames die, they leave ashes behind;
When the hen dies, it leaves hatching eggs behind;
When a warrior dies, it is fitting that he leaves behind,
something of himself." Goodbye John Mbiti.

THE END